YOUR SERVANT THE MOLECULE
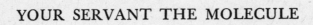

THE MACMILLAN COMPANY
NEW YORK · BOSTON · CHICAGO
DALLAS · ATLANTA · SAN FRANCISCO

MACMILLAN AND CO., LIMITED
LONDON · BOMBAY · CALCUTTA
MADRAS · MELBOURNE

THE MACMILLAN COMPANY
OF CANADA, LIMITED
TORONTO

THE ALCHEMIST

Painted 1661 by A. van Ostade (1610–1685)

Your Servant the Molecule

by

Walter S. Landis

NEW YORK

The Macmillan Company

1944

PRINTED IN THE UNITED STATES OF AMERICA
BY THE VAIL-BALLOU PRESS, INC., BINGHAMTON, N. Y.

PREFACE

Over the past years I have been repeatedly asked to name a reference book which tells the story of the chemical contributions behind the many objects that the ordinary citizen comes into contact with in his daily life.

The usual elementary text systematically lists many compounds under the respective chemical elements, but affords little help in interpreting these into the things about us. The advanced texts are too complex to be easily understood by the lay reader, the banker, the broker, the tradesman, the householder.

This little volume answers many of these inquiries. It does contain some of the jargon of the science, but the reader can readily skip over this and the chemical formulae which follow the names of the chemical compounds.

It is hoped that it will lead to a better understanding of the many applications of a most important science.

W. S. L.

CONTENTS

ILLUSTRATIONS

Chapter I

OUR DEPENDENCE ON CHEMISTRY

When you threw back the blanket this morning, you were indebted to chemistry for that soft, fleecy, colorful covering that made your night's rest comfortable. Throughout the succeeding hours of the day the chemists and the laboratories and the factories which compose the chemical industries make your life easier in countless utilitarian ways, and pleasanter in many esthetic ones. You have become so accustomed to most of these contributions that they seem a matter of course. But were man deprived of all products and processes, only the living standards of the Stone Age would be left.

Let us return to your blanket for a moment. The raw wool came from the back of a sheep, which fed and grew on the open range somewhere in the world. Nature coated its fleece with a peculiar oil or grease so that rain would roll off and not penetrate to the skin. As the sheep went about its normal open-air existence, its fleece accumulated an unbelievable quantity of trash, burs, and dirt, all tangled up in the greasy, sweaty wool. Before this wool could be converted into yarn it must be cleaned, or, as the wool processors say, *scoured*. All the foreign matter must be eliminated completely, and in most cases, the greater part of the wool-grease too. Raw wool loses as much as half its weight in scouring.

The modern way to scour wool is to dissolve the grease, but in such manner that some of the natural oil remains in the wool fiber. This requires a special type of solvent that is synthetically produced, nature not furnishing a satisfactory material. Perspiration and dirt are then washed out with water to which have been added special soaps and alkalies. Throughout this scouring operation the wool is kept in constant yet very gentle agitation to facilitate the

1

separation of the dirt and trash, but not so violent as to cause matting and felting.

The solutions in which the wool-grease has been dissolved are not thrown away. The solvent is recovered for reuse by a process of distillation not unlike the one the dry cleaner uses on his cleaning fluids, and crude grease which is left behind in the still is refined into lanolin, a valuable base for toilet preparations, shaving creams, and skin ointments.

Nor can the wash waters and rinses be poured down the drain, for if they are discharged into streams they create a most disagreeable pollution. Hence they constitute a further chemical problem, which has been solved by extracting from them whatever valuable constituents they contain, and rendering the residue harmless.

The scoured wool is graded according to the purpose for which it is to be used (in this case your blanket). It is now rather harsh and stiff, and to facilitate the mechanical operations of carding, spinning and weaving it is given a rinse in a textile oil. This is a vegetable oil or an animal fat that has been modified chemically. This textile oil not only softens the fiber of the scoured wool, but also lubricates it for passage through the modern high-speed textile machinery.

Color plays an important part in our twentieth century life, and our blanket should fit into the color schemes of our rooms. Therefore, after the blanket has been woven, the arts of the dye-maker and the dyer—two quite different kinds of chemists—are necessary. The modern fast dyes are complex chemical compounds, and the basic raw materials come from coal, or more specifically from coke ovens, and from acid and alkali plants. There are many additional auxiliary chemicals involved in the dye-making processes, intermediate between the raw materials and the finished dyes.

Fixing the prepared dye in the textile fiber so that it will not run during laundering or dry cleaning, is a highly technical process and requires differently trained chemical personnel. Even after the blanket has been through the dye house it is not yet ready for sale. It must be given a thorough washing, followed by softening and conditioning, which means more chemicals—soaps and modified oils. Industrial perfumes are added to give a pleasing odor, and moth-proofing treatment is available.

The sleeping garment you dropped on your way to the shower probably came either from a tall spruce that grew in a northern forest or possibly from lint from a southern cotton field. Chemically, the wood and the lint are near relatives. Assume, for the moment, your pajamas came from the spruce.

The chemist learned how to disintegrate wood many years ago. It is not a difficult chemical operation, and the paper manufacturer has been doing it for a long time. To break down wood it is necessary to separate the woody fiber (cellulose) from the sap (lignin bodies). First the wood is chopped into small pieces by a mechanical chipper, and these pieces or chips are cooked in a suitable chemical reagent that dissolves the sap, and can then be washed away from the fiber. Several kinds of reagents are used, depending on the kind of pulpwood. Since cotton lint contains very little sap, it is more easily and inexpensively treated than wood; but its first cost is greater.

The first step in the preparation of the lustrous yarn from which the knit or woven textile of the sleeping garment is made, is highly to purify and bleach the cellulose—or pulp, as it is more commonly called. This pulp is then treated with chemicals in several steps, and finally converted into a thick viscous solution. The solution is pumped through tiny holes in a spinneret, this submerged in a bath of acidulated liquid. The jellylike filaments would coalesce into a rod if left to themselves. Expressed into the acid liquid, they immediately set or harden as they emerge from the holes in the spinneret. The number of holes in the spinneret governs the number of filaments in the yarn—and the smaller the holes the softer and more flexible the yarn. Strict chemical controls must be exercised throughout the process to insure uniformity and continuity of the fine filaments.

The bundle of hardened filaments is then washed to remove all foreign chemicals and leave a nearly pure cellulose, after which it is ready to be made into yarn, a simple twisting operation. The yarn goes to the textile mills to be knitted or woven. In the form of a textile, it is treated much as the blanket was; but the fiber is of vegetable, not animal origin, and so different types of dyes and textile chemicals are necessary in this subsequent treatment.

When you enter the bathroom you are surrounded by the tiles, glass, porcelain, and enamel of the ceramic industry. The ceramic chemist prepares the plastic clays, glazes, and colors that withstand the heat of the pottery kiln.

Your shower curtain may be made from one of the newer synthetic products, or a modified rubber, or merely a cotton fabric, chemically treated to resist mildew.

The shiny handle on the shower valve is the result of the labor and the skill of the electrochemist. Under a thin plating of chrome or nickel is the valve body itself, made of brass—which in turn is an alloy of copper and zinc. To produce the brass, two very unlike metals had to be extracted from their ores, each involving different techniques and equipment, and then combined together. The production of metals and their alloys has become so large and important a part of our technology that it operates as an independent branch of science—metallurgy. It is founded largely on chemistry, and utilizes the same principles and laws.

From your shower issues a sparkling stream of pure water. American cities pride themselves on the quality of their water because it is free not only from water-borne disease germs, but also from sediment and color. The sanitary and biological chemists have made this possible. Chlorine and sometimes ammonia in most closely controlled amounts are introduced into the water to destroy the harmful intestinal bacteria. So also chemical coagulants which cause quick settlement of foreign matter. Continuous control is exercised to insure purity and clarity before the water is admitted to the distribution system, for should that become contaminated, correction would be extremely difficult.

To make soap our ancestors accumulated the wood ashes from their fireplaces and leached them with water, producing lye. They saved the scraps of fat from their tables and from the winter butchering. With these two ingredients, fat and lye, and in not very careful proportions, they concocted a crude soap. It was a very distant relative of our modern toilet soaps.

Today soap is made in large mechanized factories, from carefully selected vegetable oils and animal fats, carefully proportioned to the alkali, also a product of a great chemical plant. Close chemical supervision controls each step. Soaps are made in many varieties. Most of the industrial types are never encountered in the home. Bath salts, the bubble-bath, shaving soaps and creams, porcelain and tile cleaning compounds require ingredients which must be produced by other chemical manufacturing plants.

In the usual bathroom cabinet is an astounding collection of manufactured chemical products. The bicarbonate of soda is the same chemical compound that is used in the formulation of baking powder. Epsom salt is a refined form of magnesium sulphate, which is used by the carload in rayon production to set the filaments as they emerge from the spinneret. The chalk in the tooth powder is only a little whiter than that in the school crayon. Why go on? There are too many articles, and the contents of no two cabinets are the same. But in all cabinets are some simple drugs, representing the skill of still other chemists—pharmaceutical.

The creams, powders, rouges, lotions, polishes, enamels, bleaches, perfumes on feminine dressing tables are formed from a wide variety of different chemicals. Perfumes, once wholly of natural origin, are now more often synthesized than not. The cosmetic industry is one of the largest consumers of chemical products, the purity of which must be exactly determined and controlled. Hundreds of specialized chemists are continuously employed to discover and perfect new and better cosmetics, for which there is an ever growing demand.

Leather is still the basis of most of the service footwear. Tanning, dressing, and coloring of leather are chemical operations, and draw upon the manufacturing chemical industry for materials. Green hides are dehaired by means of a chemical depilatory; skins are plumped by a chemical bate. The conversion into leather employs both natural and synthetic tanning agents (these latter are complex organic and inorganic compounds) which remove certain unwanted constituents of the skin, and coagulate the fibrous portion.

Special dyes are used to color leather. Softening oils keep it flexible and prolong its wear. The enamel coating so characteristic of patent leather has the same base ingredient as fingernail polish, which in turn is a close relative of smokeless gunpowder.

Garters, girdles, rubber heels, and elastics of all kinds are products of another branch of the chemical industry. Their elasticity and toughness is due to a common ingredient, crude rubber, a natural product tapped from trees indigenous to tropical countries. But a long series of chemical operations and a great many auxiliary chemicals are required before the sap from the rubber tree becomes an elastic suitable for a garter, or a durable wear-resistant heel for a shoe.

The wartime shortage of crude rubber brought out of the chemical laboratory a variety of products which possess to some degree certain desirable properties of natural rubber. These new synthetic products are rapidly replacing the scarce natural rubber in many household uses.

The chemistry of clothes is much like that of the blanket and pajamas. But buttons, especially if they are colorful, are made of plastics. These wonderful materials can be matched to any shade, and molded into any form. Plastics have freed us from the monotony of the turned or cut button so limited in color, and afford us an almost unrestricted choice of form and hue. They exist in many varieties, and have greatly increased the variety of feminine pins, brooches, buckles, and baubles.

Almost every object encountered during the day, any day, by any person, in any occupation, has been created or modified by a chemistry that is still in its infancy.

For practical purposes we may regard chemistry as that branch of natural science which concerns itself with the composition of the materials about us, and the changes which may be brought about in this composition to form new products.

An example: Stone can laboriously be broken from a quarry,

cut to shape, and built into a house. These operations are mechanical, not chemical. Or great masses of limestone and shale may be blasted down by means of an explosive made by the chemist. If the limestone and shale are ground, and mixed in carefully controlled proportions, then burned in a kiln, and again ground to powder, the result is Portland cement. If the cement is mixed with sand and crushed stone and water, the result is concrete, a material from which the structure may be built, with an enormous saving of time and labor as compared to the cutting and chipping of stone. The cement is a product of the chemical industry, for it represents a new composition of matter. Nature gave us no such material.

Metals play an important part in our modern civilization, yet Nature has not been generous in providing them in a directly utilizable form. Iron and magnesium and aluminum, for example, are never found in the metallic state, and the same is true of lead and zinc. Only an insignificant part of the annual production of copper comes from the ground in metallic form. The iron and aluminum ores from which the metals are produced are combinations with oxygen. Copper, lead, and zinc are generally found in combination with sulphur.

The separation of these metals from their oxygen and sulphur combinations is a chemical process, for it involves a change in composition. Rolling, forging, and drawing of the metals are mechanical operations, since such shaping of the metal does not involve a change in composition.

The chemist may break down compounds into simpler components, or elements. This division is called *analytical* chemistry. The building up of simple components into more complex ones is called *synthetic* chemistry.

Analytical chemistry falls into two classifications: *qualitative* and *quantitative*. Qualitative analysis reveals the kinds or components of which a substance is composed; quantitative analysis reveals how much of each element or component is present. Once a substance has been analyzed to determine its elements, and the amount of each, it may often be duplicated at will. This permits identification of many materials that otherwise are indistinguishable. Analysis serves as an important means of standardization. It checks the purity of food products and drugs.

Synthetic chemistry creates new compounds out of simpler substances, or elements. Dyes, pharmaceuticals, plastics, and a multitude of products owe their existence to this branch of chemistry. New synthetic chemicals will always be forthcoming so long as man actively devotes himself to the pursuit of new knowledge.

One might logically assume that after a complete quantitative analysis of any substance—complete both as to the elements present and as to the percentage of each—one would have all the information necessary to define the substance exactly. In many cases this is true; but some compounds, particularly those containing carbon, cannot be completely described by such analysis. That is, there are substances which contain the same elements in identical proportions but do not have the same properties.

Most of us have seen a welder at work with his gas-burning torch, joining steel plates together. The gas burned in the torch is acetylene; and, to obtain an extremely hot flame, pure oxygen is fed into the stream of burning gas (hence the name *oxyacetylene blowtorch*). Acetylene is a compound of carbon and hydrogen, in which these two common elements are present in the proportion of 92.2 per cent carbon, and 7.8 per cent hydrogen. Commercial acetylene is a colorless gas with a characteristic odor resembling that of garlic. It is made from calcium carbide and water.

When coal is converted to coke (in a modern coke oven) a light volatile liquid distills off, called benzol; and this is a basic raw material for dyes and pharmaceutical products, and is often blended with gasoline to make an improved motor fuel. Liquid benzol contains exactly the same two elements as acetylene gas—carbon and hydrogen—in exactly the same percentages by weight.

How is it possible for these two substances containing the same elements, in identical proportions, to have such different properties? The answer is that their internal structures are differently arranged. This internal arrangement is called *constitution*. A group of compounds which have the same chemical composition but different properties are called *isomers,* and the phenomenon of like composition but different properties is called *isomerism.*

Qualitative and quantitative analysis is a highly developed art; yet much of the actual work is simple and is easily reduced to routine, particularly in control laboratories. The determination of actual structure or constitution is very complicated and often involves the application of physics as well as chemistry.

Just what is chemistry? It is that branch of natural science which deals with matter, its composition and constitution, and the changes taking place in them. Chemistry is closely related to physics, which deals with energy (the power to do work, and its transmission, transformation, and utilization). The closeness of the relationship is indicated by the fact that important divisions of the two sciences bear the titles *Physical Chemistry* and *Chemical Physics,* depending on which science is predominant. The dividing lines are not sharp. As a matter of fact, chemical changes are always accompanied by physical changes (such as change of color), by production or absorption of heat and electricity, and by many complex phenomena which have to do with the transmission and absorption of light.

Chemistry is the servant of *all* mankind, and of *all* industry. It has probably contributed most to raising the standard of living and improving the various environments of the human race. The houses in which we pass our days are constructed of chemical materials. We nourish the soil with chemicals to insure an adequate food supply. From chemicals we make the ink and the paper which enable us to preserve and disseminate knowledge. The combustion of chemicals drives our automobiles and airplanes, and generates much of the electric power that lights our cities and moves our production machinery. It is from chemicals that our photographic and motion picture film is derived. When we are well, chemicals keep us so; when we are ill, they often cure. Chemistry is, indeed, the basis of all life, for the processes of life are essentially chemical, and from the instant of birth to the moment of death we live through a continuing series of chemical reactions.

CHAPTER II

HISTORY OF THE ART

Knowledge may be divided into two great categories—art and science. Art is often associated with and used as a synonym of skill, and reaches perfection through practice (i.e., repetition). The artist, accordingly, usually has a single aim: the improvement of his skill in his chosen vocation. He is supposed to have little interest in knowledge outside his own craft, or even in the whys and wherefores of his own calling. He passes his techniques on to his successor by precept. These techniques change very slowly under such system, and only after many trials and errors. Chemistry was wholly this kind of art until three hundred years ago, and even later.

Through experimentation, careful observation, and correlation of the data obtained, one may often deduce trends or principles that can be verified to the limit one's means permit. A statement or law may be formulated that will apply generally, under a given set of circumstances. This will serve as a starting point for further investigation, without return to the fundamentals in each new research. The new experiments will add new laws (or amendments to the old laws), and in this manner a whole distinctive field of knowledge may be developed, with a concise set of principles. This is the scientific approach; it is represented by an orderly, coded set of laws for each of the several branches into which science has been divided. It offers a foundation upon which a structure of magnitude may be erected.

Robert Boyle (1627–1691), an Englishman, was the first to assemble many of the chemical ideas that had been handed down through the ages, and to review them critically in the light of his own observations of his experimental researches. He culled out the mystical and the fraudulent, and established the first of the fundamental principles of chemical science as we know it. Before his time chemistry had been wholly an art.

There is no magic in chemistry. The chemist does not employ sleight of hand in creating a new synthetic product. Every operation is subservient to scientific law. The codified laws are changed when, and only when, new facts are discovered and authenticated by experiment. Each new bit of knowledge, each new or revised law, enables the chemist to see new vistas, makes him aware of significances hitherto unsuspected. As his skill increases, and the apparatus he uses becomes more adequate and precise, he is prepared to undertake the solution of more abstruse and novel problems. He thus makes greater progress now in a few years than he formerly made in centuries. All past accomplishment is at his hand for building upon. Such is the way of science.

Nature, of course, was the first chemist. As the great mass of hot gases cooled to make this solid earth we live on, the mere cooling created substances which could not have existed at the previous higher temperatures. Weathering, in turn, broke down these newer substances, and thus created still newer compounds. That chemical process called *Life* ceaselessly creates new products, built up in marvelous complexity during the years of growth and vitality. These, too, disintegrate and are transformed by death. This is the cycle described by the preacher of old:

All are of the dust, and all turn to dust again.

First the cooling earth; then life; and then the greatest glory of all—man, with his intellect and his power to reason. Slowly, very slowly, he created the materials which would give him physical security and enhance his satisfactions.

During the Stone Age man's cunning was largely mechanical. But stone did not long satisfy his growing desires.

Man discovered metals.

There are no written records of this obliterated and inscrutable time. It is probable that the first metals man used were silver and gold, for these occur in the earliest of prehistoric remains. But silver and gold are scarce. Copper is relatively more abundant, and deposits of it are frequent on the earth's surface. The limited surface deposits of metallic copper, however, do not account for the entire supply of even these early periods. Our ancient ancestors must have developed a crude metallurgical practice, and known how to obtain copper by smelting the more abundant oxidized copper ores.

How was this learned? We can only speculate that one cold day, while he was laboriously picking out the small particles of native copper, some early man built himself a hot fire in a depression of one of the surface deposits, and later found in the ashes metal that had not been there when he began his day's work. A simple chemical reaction had occurred. The hot charcoal of the burning wood had taken the oxygen away from the copper mineral.

But copper is soft, and quickly tarnishes. A harder and more resistant metal was preferable. Later in this early age, bronze appeared. It is an alloy, a combination of copper and tin, and does not occur in nature. Tin ores are not common, yet the ancients knew of small deposits in Britain, Spain, and India. The chemical principles of early man's copper metallurgy were sufficient for smelting the two ores together.

Metallic iron is found in nature only in extremely small quantity, and in very few types of rocks. Actually there are only a few rare museum specimens. Iron in combination with oxygen, however, occurs in large deposits in many parts of the world. Iron oxides are frequently brilliant red, sometimes yellow. The ancients used them as pigments. Iron is separated from oxygen just as copper is —the chemistry of the process is the same. Because of the wide distribution of iron ores, the art of iron smelting could spread widely. It is still practiced today (in equally crude form) in remote districts of Central Africa, where the native builds a charcoal fire in a hole in the ground, puts lumps of iron ore on the coals, and, to hasten the operation, blows up his fire with crude bellows operated by hand. He also knows how to forge iron into barbed arrowheads and blades for his assagai.

We know of these early metallurgical applications of chemistry only through the archeological objects we have dug out of the ground. There may well have been other applications of chemistry; but because they lacked the permanence of metals they could not survive the devastation of time.

One of the earliest surviving allusions to chemistry occurs in the Book of Exodus:

Ye shall no more give the people straw to make brick, as heretofore: let them go and gather straw for themselves.

This refers to colloidal chemistry, a branch which has been extensively explored only in recent years, though it is of the greatest importance industrially.

Clay, from which bricks and pottery are made, is the residual product of the weathering of certain rocks. The particles of which clay is composed are extremely fine and exhibit when moistened the characteristic plasticity so important to the potter and the brick-maker. In many clay deposits the fine particles are agglomerated or clumpy, and plasticity is lacking. The clumps can be broken down or dispersed by treatment with a vegetable extract, as, for example, a water extract of straw. The Egyptians learned and practiced this knack. Today, with our better knowledge, we use a very dilute solution of caustic alkali for the same purpose. Lime, on the other hand, will produce clumps or agglomeration, or speaking technically, a flocculation of the clay particles. Hence in agriculture we lime "sticky" clay soils to *make* them crumbly, increasing drainage and aeration.

The Old Testament contains many references to chemical products. Six metals are listed: gold, silver, copper, iron, lead, and tin; also the alloy brass, although this was most likely our bronze. Joseph's coat of many colors, and robes of scarlet and of purple, connote the use of dyes. Wine and vinegar and the leavening of bread are proof of the knowledge of fermentation. Pottery, glass, lime, and mortar indicate members of a relatively extensive chemical industry.

Our word "chemistry" was undoubtedly derived from the Greek

Chemeia, which in turn came from a North Egyptian word *Cham* or *Chemi,* a name given to this geographical division of Egypt. These Egyptian forms also meant "black" or "black earth," and may have referred to black materials used in the mysterious practices of the Egyptian chemists.

The chemical processes of the Egyptians spread throughout all countries bordering on the Mediterranean, as well as into Arabia. The Greeks, about the sixth century B.C., attempted the first correlation of the existing chemical knowledge. These efforts culminated in the classic dissertations of Aristotle (384–322 B.C.).

The earliest concept of the chemical composition of the earth pictured a single mother element. One philosopher considered it to be Water; another, Air; a third, Fire. From these primitive notions developed the theory that, whatever the primary substance, it was composed of very small particles, which by combination and division, formed aggregates of various shapes and sizes that determined the character of the particular compound. It will be noticed that this bears some resemblance to the modern Atomic Theory.

Unfortunately, before the theory attained any great development, it was overshadowed by Aristotle's idea that there were four primary elements (Air, Water, Earth, and Fire) and four fundamental qualities (Hot, Cold, Dry, and Moist), and that each of the primary elements had two of these qualities at one time. By interchanging these properties, Aristotle thought, one of the elements could be converted into another. Thus, for example, water could be changed into air by abstracting cold and adding heat. He failed to recognize that in such change the water was merely converted into vapor that dispersed into the atmosphere, and there was actually no transformation.

Aristotle's theory of the transformation of the elements persisted for a long time, and was the basis of the alchemists' later search for methods by which to transmute base metals into gold. It encountered so many contradictions that he later added a fifth element, the Quintessence—a vague and elusive ethereal substance that permeated everything. But these philosophical conceptions did not seem to affect the slow progress of the chemical art. The Greeks were far advanced in medicine, and Greek chemists added many new compounds to the pharmacopoeia of the day. The chemistry of the Egyptians had been considerably enriched by Greek thought and industry before it was passed on to the Romans in the West.

Pliny the Elder, who perished in the eruption of Vesuvius at Pompeii in A.D. 79, wrote a compendium of the chemical art as it was at the beginning of the Christian Era. He had traveled over a large part of the then known world, and made an astonishing collection of the prevalent ideas and notions of natural history, medicine, chemistry, and metallurgy. His writings fill thirty-odd volumes, a half-dozen of which interest the chemist. In them Pliny described processes for the extraction and purification of metals; dyeing of textiles (including the use of mordants to fix the dye to the fibers); making of glass (and the use of metallic oxides to impart color); making of soaps, soft and hard, from fats and oils, and alkalies; and concoction of a vast variety of medicinals. He also described the production of artificial gems, and ways to recognize true stones and detect false ones.

From Pliny's time to the sixteenth century, the alchemists played a large part in the development of the chemical art. (The word "alchemist" is merely "chemist" with the Arabian prefix, *al*, meaning "the.")

From the vantage point of the twentieth century it is hardly fair to ridicule the alchemists. Among them were honest, patient seekers after knowledge, to whom the chemistry and medicine of today owe much. These men were endeavoring to solve the abstruse chemical problems with inadequate background and often with quite false notions. Their energy and effort are to be admired.

Among them, of course, were many charlatans. As in every age, they took advantage of the credulous, putting aside every scruple, even to the sacrifice of human life. Such men are by no means unknown in our day. Three projects for the transmutation of base substances into gold were promoted in New York City within the last ten or fifteen years. Each involved elaborate and complex apparatus and skilled operating personnel. One was set up and demonstrated in a technical institution of acknowledged reputation, and under the patronage of a professor (not of chemistry), by an alchemist of foreign birth. The second project was financed to the extent of half a million dollars by persons high in banking, commercial, and political circles. The third was such an involved contrivance that the controlling switchboard had almost two hundred buttons, plugs, and switches to be set before it could begin its throes of transmutation.

These modern charlatans do not confine themselves to the production of gold. They follow the daily news and try to exploit every widely publicized achievement in chemistry. And they seem to find patrons as easily as did the alchemists of old.

The honest and sincere alchemists of the Middle Ages should not be disparaged because of the charlatans. Some of their errors are quite explicable. They did not know that the ores of mercury and lead quite frequently also contain silver and gold. Analytical chemistry had not yet been developed. When they evaporated mercury, or oxidized lead, and found residues of gold and silver, the conclusion that they had transmuted a base metal was practically inevitable.

The belief arose that there must be some one substance—possibly some chemical compound—which, when brought into contact with base metals, turns them into gold. A name was given to this magical substance: the Philosopher's Stone. All alchemists sought it; many were sure they had found it. An extension of the idea of the Philosopher's Stone led to the conception of an Elixir of Youth, a substance which would prolong life indefinitely.

The alchemists started with many handicaps, not entirely of their own creation. The Egyptians had infused their chemistry with mysticism and astrology; Plato (427–347 B.C.) fathered a philosophy that real things are sorry imitations of perfect essences (archetypes) existing in some extramundane world; Aristotle and his quintessence—all these certainly did not further scientific development along the lines of organized observation and experiment.

By the time universities were established in Europe, the alchemists were turning their attention from the search for the Philosopher's Stone and the Elixir of Youth to the preparation of drugs and pharmaceuticals. Again a new theory of the composition of matter gripped men's minds. It was thought that all matter, living or dead, was composed of three elements—mercury, sulphur, and salt—these three elemental substances representing the fundamental qualities of fluidity, combustibility, and rigidity. Illness resulted from increase or decrease of these essential elements. If more than the normal amount of sulphur accumulated in the body, fever and plague ensued; a deficiency of mercury caused gout; too much mercury brought on melancholia and rheumatism.

Such ideas were quite dangerous. Even honest physicians killed their patients by treating disease in accordance with them. Many medicines concocted by the alchemists contained strong poisons, which were given to human beings quite innocently to cure, not kill.

Out of this preoccupation, however, much valuable knowledge was gained. The difference between acids and alkalies was recognized. Salts were produced by combining an acid with a base. More precise records of the vast experimentation were kept. The foundations of modern chemistry were laid.

Reference has been made to the Englishman Robert Boyle, sometimes called the "father of modern chemistry." He was a man of wealth, which he employed to advance scientific discovery. He was a founder of the British Royal Society, the oldest scientific organization in the world still in existence, with its unbroken series of transactions published since 1665. One of his discoveries is known to every schoolboy: Boyle's Law (the volume of every gas varies inversely with the pressure, the temperature being held constant).

Boyle espoused the new kind of learning Francis Bacon (1561–1626) was then publicizing. Boyle insisted that chemists should collect data, make experiments, but advance no new theories until every related phenomenon had been investigated thoroughly. He did not believe that all matter was composed of mercury, salt, and sulphur, but thought that there were *many* substances, not merely three, which could not be broken down into simpler things. He predicted that many more such simple substances would be discovered in the future. It was Boyle who suggested that these substances be called *elements*.

But just when such an excellent start was being made in the chemical science, a new and false theory about combustion and oxidation spread throughout Europe and even to the new America—one which did not disappear until the beginning of the nineteenth century. During its ascendancy many of the leading chemists believed in it and promoted it. This theory assumed that a metallic element is composed of a *kalk* or *calx,* and *phlogiston.* When the metal is heated, the phlogiston is driven off, and the earthy material, or kalk, which remains is different for each element. Charcoal was considered to be nothing but phlogiston, for when charcoal is burned, nothing remains. When the kalk (an oxide to the modern chemist) was heated with charcoal, this was presumed to have transferred its phlogiston to the kalk, and so reformed the metal.

The interest in phlogiston was intense, and the search for this most elusive substance led to the development of the accurate chemical balance and to exhaustive research in the field of quantitative analysis. The Swedish chemist Scheele (1742–1786), in the course of his investigations on combustion, discovered the elements nitrogen, oxygen, manganese and barium, many mineral acids, and even explored the almost untouched field of organic compounds. The English chemist Priestley (1733–1804), independently of Scheele, discovered oxygen at about the same time, also the several oxides of nitrogen, gaseous hydrochloric acid, gaseous ammonia, sulphur dioxide. Priestley was a devoted adherent of the phlogiston school; Scheele, somewhat of a skeptic.

The French chemist Lavoisier (1743–1794) dealt a mortal blow to the phlogiston theory. He was highly educated in mathematics and physics as well as botany and chemistry, and was a most critical observer. He used the chemical balance in his experimental work, and carried out chemical and physical reactions in sealed glass vessels. He proved the conservation of matter in these physical and chemical reactions. Applying his discoveries to the chemistry of oxidation and combustion, he found no place for the elusive phlogiston; and the theory did not long survive his attack. Lavoisier was head of the French saltpeter (potassium nitrate) and gunpowder plants, a member of numerous governmental commissions, and contributed a great deal to the application of chemistry to many fields of commercial activity.

The idea of the atomic constitution of matter was only qualitatively developed by Boyle. The English chemist Dalton (1766–1844), on the foundation laid by Boyle to the effect that chemical compounds were formed by the union of very small particles or "corpuscles" of the elements, concluded that the numbers of these "atoms," as he called them, were always the same in the same compound. Since like compounds always showed the same percentage weights of the elements composing them, the atom of any element must always have the same combining weight. Assuming unity for the weight of a hydrogen atom, Dalton constructed a table of the combining weights of many of the elements then known.

Using greatly perfected analytical methods, Berzelius (1779–1848), a Swede, corrected many of the figures of the Dalton table, leaving no possible place for phlogiston in the chemical compound. Dalton had announced several laws governing the combination of elements to form compounds; but there was much confusion in their application, and the atomic weights of Dalton's day do not correspond with those we now use for many of the elements. A succession of physicists began to apply their science to the problem of chemical combination, and the phenomenon of combining power—valence, as it is now called—became an associated property of the atom.

The bitter dispute as to the existence and nature of phlogiston was not without profit. In the search, many new elements were discovered, new compounds were made, new laws were formulated. Phlogiston passed out of the chemical scene near the end of the eighteenth century; but during the one hundred fifty years of controversy the industrial phase of chemistry had advanced greatly.

Most of the common metals had been discovered, even bismuth and zinc. Also a number of the nonmetallic elements. Silver was, for the first time, separated from its alloy with gold by the aid of strong acids. The amalgamating process of extracting silver from complex ores was in operation in Mexico. Enamels and glazes were greatly perfected, as in the beautiful faïence ware of the day. The Italians had greatly improved the variety and quality of glass, and exhibited great skill in coloring it.

Mineral acids—sulphuric, nitric, and muriatic—were manufactured in quantity. Their action on metals produced many new compounds. Ammonia and many of its salts were articles of commerce. New countries opened up by the intensive exploration of the times gave many new dyes of vegetable origin to the textile industry, and presented new problems of application. The use of mordants became common.

Even the field of organic chemistry began to be explored in a systematic manner. Pure alcohol, glycerine, and a few organic acids were produced. Some degree of correlation of mineral and organic chemistry had been attained. The way was opened for the remarkable progress made during the nineteenth century in the new science.

Chapter III

THE SCIENCE

Like all branches of science chemistry has its jargon, which cannot be avoided entirely. If the reader will learn a little of it now, he will find the rest of the book easier to understand.

The name by which scientists describe all material things—wood, iron, oxygen, gasoline, stone—is *matter*.

All matter has certain characteristics. It occupies space, it has weight, it cannot be destroyed (though it can be altered in form —for example, the two gases oxygen and hydrogen may exist separately, or may be combined in the form of liquid water).

Matter occurs in three principal physical forms:

Solid: characterized by definite shape or rigidity, and with definite boundary or volume.

Liquid: having no rigidity, but of definite volume. A liquid takes the shape of the containing vessel. The top surface of a liquid at rest is always level.

Gaseous: having neither rigidity nor definite volume. Irrespective of its amount, a gas *always* fills the container.

There is a transition stage between the solid and the liquid states called *viscous*. A very thick liquid which only slowly becomes immobile is viscous. There is also a transition stage between liquid and gaseous states, called the *critical state*. It is rarely encountered in industrial chemistry, in which viscous forms are quite common.

A mass that is uniform throughout in composition and structure is said to be *homogeneous*. Granulated sugar, and a solution of salt in water, are typical examples of homogeneous matter. Matter in which unlike components are present is called a *mixture;* for example, salt and pepper together.

Solids may be classified in still another way. Homogeneous sol-

21

ids occur frequently with sharp edges and smooth faces at definite angles to one another. These are called *crystals*. They occur in nature in cavities of rocks, and are very common in products manufactured by man. They form from a molten mass, on cooling, or from a saturated solution. Well formed crystals usually indicate purity.

Another kind of solid has no definite structure; for example, rosin, or glue. This type of solid is called *amorphous*. Most of the solids in the amorphous form are of very complex chemical constitution.

A *chemical compound* is a substance combining two or more elements in definite, unvarying proportions. It is homogeneous, and may be solid, liquid, or gaseous; crystalline or amorphous. For example, every grain or crystal of common salt contains two elements, sodium and chlorine, in the proportions 39.3 per cent sodium and 60.7 per cent chlorine.

A lump of sugar placed in a glass of water will disappear, leaving a clear homogeneous liquid. Such a liquid mixture, no matter what the proportions of the materials, is called a *solution*. There are a few examples of homogeneous solids whose composition varies: for example, glass. These are called *solid solutions*.

At Niagara Falls thousands of tons of rock salt, shipped from the mines near Syracuse, New York, are converted into a soft white metal which tarnishes quickly in the air (sodium), and a yellowish gas of vicious choking nature (chlorine). A great deal of electric energy is required to break up the salt into these constituents, the energy coming from the power plants at the Falls.

Rock salt is a white crystalline compound with no distinguishing characteristics that suggest the presence of the metal and the gas. If a grain is broken in two pieces, each is still salt. If grains are ground in a mill to the very finest powder, it is still salt, particle for particle, by taste, by analysis. One can imagine a grain ground so fine as to produce a salt particle that could not be divided any more and remain salt. This would be the *molecule* of salt—the smallest particle of a chemical compound that possesses all the properties of that compound.

No one has ever seen a molecule, even the largest, under the most powerful microscope yet constructed.

Molecules in turn are built from *atoms*. Atoms are the smallest particles of an element.

Now it does not matter how much salt passes through this plant at Niagara Falls (a pound, a ton, a trainload): 60.7 per cent of its weight will be chlorine, and 39.3 per cent by weight will be sodium. These must be the proportions in the molecule. This can mean only one thing: that each atom of sodium and each atom of chlorine must possess a definite weight, and the number of atoms of each that combine to make the salt molecule must always be the same. Otherwise the chemical composition would vary, which is contrary to the observed facts.

This is a matter of such fundamental importance that chemists have spent enormous amounts of time and ingenuity to determine the weights of the atoms of the elements. The actual weights, however, are so extremely small and so inconvenient to use in commercial work that an arbitrary scale has been devised. The lightest atom is that of hydrogen, and the weight of its atom has been arbitrarily fixed at 1. The weights of the atoms of the other ninety-one elements are expressed as multiples of this unit value for hydrogen. The actual weight of the hydrogen atom is approximately 0.000,000,000,000,000,000,000,000,036,5 pounds. The atom of the heaviest element, Uranium weighs only 238 times that of hydrogen.

Of late years the atomic weights have been expressed as multiples of the weight of oxygen (which is arbitrarily assumed as 16.00), largely because oxygen occurs in more chemical compounds than hydrogen.

The avidity with which atoms unite to form chemical compounds indicates a strong attraction of one atom for another. When carbon (for example, charcoal) unites with oxygen to form carbon dioxide, as in ordinary combustion, a great amount of heat is generated. The decomposition of common salt into its elements, sodium and chlorine, requires a large amount of electrical energy, this being the reverse of formation. This attraction between the elements is called *affinity,* and is believed to be electrical in nature.

The measure of this affinity is called *valence.* Again the hydrogen atom is arbitrarily assumed to have a valence of 1, and the atoms of the other elements have valences of 1 to 8, according to their power to combine with 1 to 8 atoms of hydrogen. For example, oxygen has a valence of 2, since it is combined with two hydrogen atoms in water.

Forces of attraction, energy, electricity are physical manifestations, and the physicist has naturally played the more important role in determining the structure of the atom, and the influence of this structure on its behavior. It is believed that all atoms are alike, in that they are composed of positive charged units, called protons, negative units, called electrons, and neutral units, called neutrons.

The core of the atom, called the nucleus, is composed of protons and neutrons, and it is in the nucleus that the weight of the atom is concentrated. The electrons revolve about the nucleus in regular orbits, and at very high speed. The number of electrons equals the number of protons—so that the atom is electrically neutral— and is the same as the atomic number (see Table, page 28).

When atoms of two different elements are brought into close association, one may give up an electron to the other. This leaves the first electrically unbalanced with an extra proton; the receiving atom will have an extra negative charge. This sets up an attraction between the two atoms, and chemical union results. Atoms which give up an electron readily, assuming a positive electrical charge, are said to have a plus valence. The atoms of the metals and hydrogen all have *plus* valences. Atoms which most readily take on electrons, thereby assuming a negative charge, are said to have *minus* valence. There are some elements in which the atoms may either give up or take on electrons, depending on the surrounding conditions; these may be of either plus or minus valence.

It is quite evident that in any stable chemical compound, formed by the union of atoms as described, the valences of the atoms composing it must balance. That is, for each plus valence there must be a corresponding minus valence. In the jargon of the chemical laboratory these balanced plus and minus valences are called bonds, and in picturing the structure of his chemical compounds, the chemist indicates them by a short stroke.

The determination of atomic weights is largely a matter of precise and painstaking chemical analysis. Only the most carefully purified chemical compounds can be used as starting materials. The procedure for chlorine, for example, is to take a sample of very pure hydrochloric acid, and by several methods analyze it for hydrogen and chlorine, its two constituents. Result: hydrogen, 2.74 per cent; chlorine, 97.26 per cent. Or one may synthesize pure hydrogen and pure chlorine into hydrochloric acid, carefully weighing the quantity of each beforehand. These quantities would be in the same ratio as the figures given above. Since the hydrogen atom was assumed to have a single plus valence, there could be only a single valence, that is a single atom of chlorine in the combination. Therefore the weight ratio of the hydrogen atom to the chlorine atom is 2.74:97.26 or 1:35.5 Since the atomic weight of the hydrogen atom was assumed as unity, the atomic weight of the chlorine is 35.5.

As methods and equipment improve, it is necessary from time to time to correct the tables of atomic weights. The changes are passed upon by an international commission each second year. In late years most of the changes are in second and third decimal places. Atomic weights are involved in all the calculations involved in chemical processing and in analysis. Atomic weight is as important to the chemist as a measuring rule is to the mechanic or engineer. Slide rules for chemical calculations have atomic weight scales.

At the present time man knows of ninety-two different kinds of atoms: that is, ninety-two different elements. It is more than possible that one or two more may be discovered in the future.

Ten of these ninety-two elements make up 99 per cent of all the matter on earth. Half of the earth's crust is oxygen (in combination with something else, for only a small amount occurs by itself in the atmosphere); 26 per cent is silicon; 7 per cent is aluminum; 4 per cent, iron; and 2 per cent or less, each of the following: magnesium, sodium, potassium, hydrogen, and titanium. Some of the ninety-two elements are extremely rare. Outside a chemical museum, the average man won't see a third of the number during his whole life.

The names of the elements are different in different countries. This would make it difficult for chemists to understand one another were it not for a set of symbols universally used to designate the elements. These symbols for the older known elements consist of the first letter, or the first two letters, of their Latin names. Thus the symbol for gold is Au because the Latin name of this metal is *aurum*. To an English chemist, Au means exactly what it does to a French one, even though the Englishman calls it "gold" and the Frenchman *or*. The symbol for iron is Fe because the Latin name of this metal is *ferrum*. For many of the elements discovered in recent centuries, the first letter of the name is the symbol, as O for oxygen, H for hydrogen, C for carbon. Sometimes two letters of the name are necessary to prevent confusion, as Cl for chlorine.

Symbols are also used to designate the chemical compounds. Since the compounds are combinations of atoms, the symbols of the elements are employed. Instead of writing "sodium chloride" for common table salt, the chemist writes NaCl: Na is the symbol for sodium (Latin *natrium*). NaCl is much shorter, and even more explicit, for it indicates the composition—one atom of sodium combined with one atom of chlorine; and it serves as the symbol of the molecule of the compound. Hydrochloric acid consists of one atom of hydrogen (symbol H) and one atom of chlorine (symbol Cl). Therefore the symbol of the molecule of hydrochloric acid is written HCl. Sulphuric acid consists of two atoms of hydrogen, one of sulphur (symbol S), and four of oxygen. Therefore the molecule of sulphuric acid is H_2SO_4. To indicate *two molecules* of sulphuric acid, the number 2 is placed before the symbol H_2SO_4: 2 H_2SO_4. Water consists of two atoms of hydrogen and one atom of oxygen, and therefore the symbol for a molecule of water is H_2O.

A group of symbols indicating a compound is called a *formula*.

The list, pp. 28–9, of the ninety-two elements gives the names by which they are known in the United States. The second column contains the symbols by which they are known all over the world. The third column contains the *atomic numbers*—the numbers of electrons contained in each atom. With one or two exceptions it is essentially the order of their ascending atomic weights. Again, with these same exceptions, it is interesting to note that every eighth number denotes similar elements. The fourth column contains the atomic weights, rounded off to a single decimal place, a precision quite sufficient for industrial work. The fifth column contains the valences of the atoms. Note that some elements have more than one valence; that is, they readily yield more than one number of electrons.

For a long time the field of chemistry was divided into the chemistry of the mineral world, *inorganic* chemistry, and the chemistry of the living world, *organic* chemistry. The same fundamental laws and principles govern both fields. Life is no longer regarded as necessary to the formation of many compounds that were once considered to be derived solely through living plants or animals. Many such compounds are now synthesized in the laboratory, and the number is continually increasing. Organic chemistry is better called the chemistry of the carbon compounds, for the element carbon is found in all characteristic organic compounds. The number of known organic compounds is in the hundreds of thousands, that is, many times that of the inorganic compounds.

The inorganic compounds are divided into three classes: *acids, bases,* and *salts.*

Acids are compounds that contain hydrogen in such combination that it can be displaced by a metal. The common strong acids are sulphuric, H_2SO_4; hydrochloric, HCl; and nitric, HNO_3. They taste sour (be certain they are diluted before trying), and they are very corrosive. They dissolve metals. They alter the color of many vegetable dyes. Other inorganic acids are quite mild, like carbonic, H_2CO_3; boric, H_3BO_3. Some acids are more common as *anhydrides* —with their water elements eliminated. For example, the anhydride silica, SiO_2, forms more than half the earth, but in the acid form is so unstable that it is rarely found outside the laboratory.

TABLE OF ELEMENTS

NAME	SYMBOL	ATOMIC NUMBER	ATOMIC WEIGHT	VALENCE
Actinium	Ac	89	227	3
Alabamine	Ab	85	221	1, 3, 5, 7
Aluminum	Al	13	27	3
Antimony	Sb	51	121.8	3, 5
Argon	A	18	40	0
Arsenic	As	33	74.9	3, 5
Barium	Ba	56	137.4	2
Beryllium	Be	4	9	2
Bismuth	Bi	83	209	3, 5
Boron	B	5	10.8	3
Bromine	Br	35	79.9	1, 3, 5, 7
Cadmium	Cd	48	112.4	2
Calcium	Ca	20	40	2
Carbon	C	6	12	2, 4
Cerium	Ce	58	140.1	3, 4
Cesium	Cs	55	132.9	1
Chlorine	Cl	17	35.4	1, 3, 5, 7
Chromium	Cr	24	52	2, 3, 6
Cobalt	Co	27	58.9	2, 3
Columbium	Cb	41	92.9	3, 5
Copper	Cu	29	63.6	1, 2
Dysprosium	Dy	66	162.5	3
Erbium	Er	68	167	3
Europium	Eu	63	152	2, 3
Fluorine	F	9	19	1
Gadolinium	Gd	64	156.9	3
Gallium	Ga	31	69.7	2, 3
Germanium	Ge	32	72.6	4
Gold	Au	79	197.2	1, 3
Hafnium	Hf	72	178.6	4
Helium	He	2	4	0
Holmium	Ho	67	163.5	3
Hydrogen	H	1	1.00	1
Illinium	Il	61	146	3
Indium	In	49	114.8	3
Iodine	I	53	126.9	1, 3, 5, 7
Iridium	Ir	77	193	3, 4
Iron	Fe	26	55.8	2, 3
Krypton	Kr	36	83.7	0
Lanthanum	La	57	138.9	3
Lead	Pb	82	207.2	2, 4
Lithium	Li	3	6.9	1
Lutecium	Lu	71	175	3
Magnesium	Mg	12	24.3	2
Manganese	Mn	25	54.9	2, 3, 4, 6, 7
Masurium	Ma	43	?	?

Name	Symbol	Atomic Number	Atomic Weight	Valence
Mercury	Hg	80	200.6	1, 2
Molybdenum	Mo	42	96	3, 4, 6
Neodymium	Nd	60	144.3	3
Neon	Ne	10	20.2	0
Nickel	Ni	28	58.7	2, 3
Nitrogen	N	7	14	3, 5
Osmium	Os	76	190.2	2, 3, 4, 8
Oxygen	O	8	16.00	2
Palladium	Pd	46	106.7	2, 4
Phosphorus	P	15	31	3, 5
Platinum	Pt	78	195.2	3
Polonium	Po	84	210	—
Potassium	K	19	39.1	1
Praseodymium	Pr	59	140.9	3
Protoactinium	Pa	91	231	—
Radium	Ra	88	226	2
Radon	Rn	86	222	0
Rhenium	Re	75	186.3	—
Rhodium	Rh	45	102.9	3
Rubidium	Rb	37	85.5	1
Ruthenium	Ru	44	101.7	3, 4, 6, 8
Samarium	Sa	62	150.4	3
Scandium	Sc	21	45.1	3
Selenium	Se	34	79	2, 4, 6
Silicon	Si	14	28	4
Silver	Ag	47	107.9	1
Sodium	Na	11	23	1
Strontium	Sr	38	87.6	2
Sulphur	S	16	32	2, 4, 6
Tantalum	Ta	73	180.9	2, 4, 6
Tellurium	Te	52	127.6	2, 4, 6
Terbium	Tb	65	159.2	3
Thallium	Tl	81	204.4	1, 3
Thorium	Th	90	232.1	4
Thulium	Tm	69	169.4	3
Tin	Sn	50	118.7	2, 4
Titanium	Ti	22	48	3, 4
Tungsten	W	74	183.9	6
Uranium	U	92	238	4, 6
Vanadium	V	23	51	3, 5
Virginium	Vi	87	224	1
Xenon	Xe	54	131.3	0
Ytterbium	Yb	70	173	3
Yttrium	Y	39	88.9	3
Zinc	Zn	30	65.4	2
Zirconium	Zr	40	91.2	4

In its acid form it is known as silicic acid, H_4SiO_4 (also written $2 H_2O \cdot SiO_2$—that is, two molecules of water and one molecule of silica).

Bases are oxides and hydroxides of the metals. Some common oxides are ferric oxide, Fe_2O_3, the most common ore of iron; zinc oxide, ZnO, a common ingredient of white paint; calcium oxide, CaO, ordinary quicklime. *Hydroxides* are compounds containing hydroxyl, —OH, instead of the oxygen of the oxides. Hydroxyl is a *radical*—that is, a group of two or more elements which act as a unit, as though they were a single element. Because the valence of oxygen is 2, two hydroxyls must substitute for each oxygen atom. Some examples are magnesium hydroxide, $Mg(OH)_2$, common household milk of magnesia; ammonium hydroxide, NH_4OH, sometimes called aqua ammonia and, in dilute form, household ammonia; caustic soda, NaOH, the lye of the soapmaker.

Salts result from the combination of acids and bases. Therefore they consist of a metal derived from the base, and the *characteristic* portion of the acid. Their formation may be illustrated in symbolic form:

$$Ca(OH)_2 \ + \ H_2SO_4 \ = \ CaSO_4 \ + \ 2 H_2O$$

| calcium hydroxide | sulphuric acid | | calcium sulphate | water |

A salt may also be made directly from a metal:

$$Zn \ + \ 2 HCl \ = \ ZnCl_2 \ + \ H_2$$

| zinc | hydrochloric acid | | zinc chloride | hydrogen |

Symbolic representations like the above are called *chemical equations*. They depict chemical changes, which are called *reactions*.

Chemical equations are usually so written that the left-hand side represents the materials undergoing chemical transformation (called *reagents* or *reactants*). The right-hand side represents the *products* of the reaction. Before a valid chemical equation can be written, the identity of the products must be determined either by observation or by chemical analysis. The more skilled the chemist, and the more familiar he is with the laws of chemistry and of the properties of many compounds, the less he needs of complete or even partial analysis of the products before he can write the equation.

These equations are more than mere chemical shorthand. For example, in the first equation above, in which calcium hydroxide reacts with sulphuric acid, the *quantities* of the reagents and the products are indicated by the molecular weights, which are in turn the sums of the weights of all the atoms in each compound. The molecular weight of calcium hydroxide is $40 + 2(16 + 1) = 74$; that of sulphuric acid $2 \times 1 + 32 + 4 \times 16 = 98$; that of calcium sulphate $40 + 32 + 4 \times 16 = 136$; of water $2 \times 1 + 16 = 18$. The quantities may be in any units (tons, pounds, or grams), in any system of weights, so long as all are in the same unit. In other words 74 pounds of calcium hydroxide will react with 98 pounds of pure sulphuric acid to make 136 pounds of calcium sulphate and 18 pounds of water. This is only one application of these very useful equations.

Chemical reactions do not always completely utilize the reagents. Sometimes reactions are very slow. Effective stirring may speed them up. Changes of temperature, either heating or cooling, may change the course of the reaction. Pressure often has a marked effect. The concentration of the solutions employed is an important factor in the character and the course of a reaction. The skilled chemist, by a suitable choice of all these factors, will influence the course of his reactions so as to obtain the maximum yields of the desired products, in the quickest possible time.

Chemical reactions are usually accompanied by the generation or absorption of heat. Throw quicklime, CaO, into a small amount of water to form the slaked lime, calcium hydroxide, $Ca(OH)_2$, and enough heat is evolved to boil the water. Chemists have tables listing the thermal properties of most compounds and know in advance when heating will be needed to promote a reaction, or when cooling is necessary to carry off an excess of heat generated during the course of a reaction. *Thermochemistry* is an important branch of chemical knowledge.

Chemical reactions are frequently accompanied by distinctive changes of color. Many dyes change color with the degree of acidity or alkalinity of their solutions. Solutions can be analyzed by measuring the absorption of infrared and of ultraviolet rays, absorption bands being specific for individual compounds. The involved chemistry of the photographic image depends on the influence of light on a mixture of gelatin, silver chloride, and silver bromide.

A chemical reaction between solids is difficult to bring about. A few mixtures, principally unstable compounds belonging to the class of explosives, will react as solids. In most cases the solids must be put into solution to bring about a reaction. When an acid, base, or salt is dissolved in water, there is a slackening or loosening of the bonds holding the molecule together. This phenomenon is called *ionization,* and is all-important in causing a chemical reaction.

When two or more solutions are mixed, one of the most noticeable results is the formation of an insoluble compound that settles out, called a *precipitate.* Such a compound will not dissolve in the solvent, and drops out of the solution as a crystal, powder, curd, or gel, depending on its individual characteristics. It can be recovered by allowing it to settle, or by filtering it through a porous material—paper, cloth, even certain kinds of stoneware.

Some chemical reactions occur very fast, like the explosion of gunpowder, or of dynamite. Others take hours, even days, like the rag saturated with linseed oil left behind by the careless painter. The oil slowly oxidizes in the air, producing heat which in time causes flame. In general chemical reactions are speeded by increase of temperature. An increase of 20° Fahrenheit will double the velocity of some reactions. When the reaction is carried out in a water-solution in an open tank, the heating is limited by the temperature at which the water boils out of the solution, that is to somewhat over 212° F. If higher temperatures are required, closed vessels capable of withstanding the desired pressures of the steam must be used. This is the principle underlying the pressure cooker in the kitchen. In the chemical industry, pressure vessels are called *autoclaves,* and can withstand many thousands of pounds per square inch.

Reactions involving gases can sometimes be speeded by using

high pressures, sometimes by using less than atmospheric pressure. Chemical laws determine the preferred conditions. In a chemical reaction between gases, if the volume of the products is less than the volume of the reagents, high pressure speeds the reaction; if the volume of the products is greater than the volume of the reagents, pressures below atmospheric may be more favorable.

Reactions may be favored by the use of a *catalyst*—a substance which speeds a chemical reaction but is itself not changed thereby. An example is a form of cigarette lighter that consists of a straight tubular body with a shallow hollow top for insertion of a cigarette: a few puffs on the cigarette, and the inserted end lights. In the body of the tube is a wad of cotton or some other absorbent material saturated with methanol, CH_3OH (once called wood spirit or wood alcohol). In the upper end of the tube is a very small mass of platinum in porous or spongy form, and supported on a wire grid. Just under the platinum spot is a hole to admit air. The end of the cigarette is inserted until it just touches the platinum spot. The puff draws in air which mixes with vapor given off by the volatile methanol, and this vapor-air mixture in contact with the platinum, actually starts reacting at ordinary temperatures, heats the platinum red-hot, and lights the cigarette. The methanol-air mixture would not react of itself at ordinary temperatures, but in the presence of the platinum, oxidation is so speeded up that actual burning is taking place on the surface of the spongy platinum. The platinum sponge is a catalytic agent; it is not consumed and, unless damaged mechanically, lasts a long time.

Catalytic agents are most often solid porous masses, but some exist in liquid form. They are of great importance in industrial chemistry, particularly in the production of sulphuric acid, nitric acid, ammonia, alcohol, and a large number of organic preparations; and in the field of organic chemistry several of the most modern oil-refining steps use catalysts on a very large scale.

There are many theories as to the exact mechanism of catalytic action. It is apparently a phenomenon associated with surface; most of the solid catalysts have a very porous structure and thus present the maximum of surface. Catalyst compositions vary with the purpose for which they are to be used, and chemists have catalogued the catalytic activity of many elements and compounds effective in oxidation, hydrogenation, dehydration, synthesis, etc. By their use reactions can be made to take place at commercial speeds, and at temperatures so low that there is little danger of decomposing sensitive products.

Anticatalysts are also employed to retard chemical reactions which are not desired.

A chemical reaction involving a gas or vapor is simpler to deal with mathematically than one involving solids or liquids. In commerce gases are usually sold by volume, and the gas meter is the common measuring device. That gas reactions involve simple volume relationships has been known for a hundred years. The quantities of reagents and of products, expressed in volume units, are in the ratios of whole numbers, 1 to 2, 2 to 3, etc. The molecules of *all* gases have the *same* volume when measured at the same temperature and pressure.

In a chemical equation for a reaction involving gases, the number of molecules of each reagent and each product indicates the volume of each reagent and product. Most of the common gaseous elements—hydrogen, oxygen, nitrogen, chlorine, etc.—have two atoms in each molecule, and they are placed in the equation as H_2, O_2, N_2, Cl_2, etc. For example, the common welding torch burns acetylene, C_2H_2, with oxygen, O_2 (the gases acetylene and oxygen being contained in steel cylinders under high pressures). The reaction in the flame is

$$2\,C_2H_2 + 5\,O_2 = 4\,CO_2 + 2\,H_2O$$

Since the equation shows two molecules of acetylene for five molecules of oxygen, the welder provides himself with two and one-half times as much oxygen as acetylene.

Since the volumes of all gaseous molecules are the same at the same temperature and pressure, it naturally follows that the volume of a molecular weight of any gas is a constant. The volume of a molecular weight of any gas or vapor, expressed in pounds, is 359 cubic feet, if measured at a temperature of 32° F. and under a pressure of one atmosphere—14.7 pounds per square inch absolute. From the weight of a carefully measured volume of gas or vapor, it is possible to calculate its molecular weight; from the weights of like volumes of several gases containing the same element, it is possible to calculate atomic weights.

The few principles set forth here illustrate the precision and the breadth of the laws that govern the science of chemistry. Voluminous texts are required to present all the laws that control chemical reactions and related phenomena. The chemist is always faced with the question, Will a given chemical reaction take place? If so, under what conditions, and what will be the yield of products from a given amount of reagents? Stated in another form, will the two reagents x and y (which seem to be logical raw materials from which to make the product z) react, and under what conditions of temperature, pressure, and concentration? The answers to many such questions can be obtained, when the fundamental data are available, by mathematical calculation.

The driving force in all chemical reactions is a change in energy relationships. Reactions readily take place if thereby energy is set free, either as of heat or as electricity. In the acetylene torch mentioned above, the union of oxygen and acetylene liberates a large amount of heat, and such a reaction, if started by lighting a match, proceeds rapidly to completion. The amount of energy likely to be released during the course of a reaction can be calculated. By calculation the chemist selects in advance the most suitable conditions for a reaction.

For two hundred years chemists have been accumulating such data and calculations, classifying them, and evolving a code of chemical law. New information is added each year, resulting in revision, expansion, and broader applications. This is the principal reason why the chemical industry can create new products, substitute materials, meet new demands, add to the nation's wealth.

Chapter IV

ORGANIC CHEMISTRY

For several thousand years man has made medicines out of roots, herbs, and flowers. And for a long time he has used extracts of vegetable origin in tanning leather and dyeing textiles. The early chemists and their successors, the alchemists, isolated and identified some of these compounds of animal and vegetable origin; but it was not until the seventeenth century that a small catalogue of such compounds was published. Very little was then known about their composition, and less about their constitution. They were called *organic compounds* because it was thought that they could only be produced through some process of life.

An increasing number of chemists gave more and more attention to these organic products, and early in the nineteenth century several well known and characteristic "organics" were actually made in the laboratory from materials and by methods that involved no living process. Thus the old classification lost its original significance, though it is still retained today in the lecture hall and the textbook.

Organic chemistry is now defined as concerning the compounds of carbon and hydrogen and their derivatives, for in *all* organic compounds carbon is the characteristic element. Secondary elements are hydrogen, oxygen, nitrogen, and sulphur. A few typical organic groups are combined with metallic elements; these are called metallo-organic compounds.

Paint vehicles, varnishes, lacquers and enamels, soaps and perfumes, petroleum and motor fuels, rubber, dyes, pharmaceuticals —all are or contain organic compounds. Billions of dollars' worth are sold and consumed each year. Organic chemistry is the most active branch of the chemical industry, and is the most favored and prolific field of research. Inorganic chemistry supplies the acids, alkalies, salts, and other chemical auxiliaries that make organic chemical production possible.

Carbon occurs in nature in several forms: as diamonds; more abundantly as graphite; and very plentifully as coal. Most organic compounds when heated in a retort in the absence of air leave behind a char, or mass of carbon. The charcoal we use to grill our steak is such a residue (from distilling wood). All forms of carbon when heated to a very high temperature are converted ultimately to graphite, which seems to be the most stable form of carbon.

Carbon has a valence of 4 in its combinations (there is one compound carbon monoxide, CO, in which the valence appears to be 2). The four valences act in space at equal angles with one another (approximately 109°). A space arrangement is difficult to represent on a plane surface like this sheet of paper. The symbol $-\overset{|}{\underset{|}{C}}-$ is the best that can be done with print. It is in common usage for illustrating the carbon structure in organic compounds. For example, the structure of the molecule of the gas methane, CH_4, which is also called marsh gas (because decaying vegetable matter produces it), is symbolized by $H-\overset{\overset{\displaystyle H}{|}}{\underset{\underset{\displaystyle H}{|}}{C}}-H$.

Carbon combines with both hydrogen and oxygen, yet these two atoms have valences of opposite character, for they combine together to form water. This fact that the valences of carbon may be either plus or minus makes for great facility of combination. Another unique property of the carbon atom is its ability to combine with another carbon atom. Sometimes a string of carbon atoms will combine in chain fashion, sometimes in a ring. These unusual characteristics of the carbon atom are chiefly responsible for the fact that there are many times more carbon, or organic, compounds than inorganic ones.

Since carbon is in all organic compounds, it would not be very descriptive merely to call them carbon compounds. There is a more illuminating way to classify them.

A compound containing only carbon and hydrogen is called a *hydrocarbon*. There are three principal classes of hydrocarbons: (1) aliphatic, alkyl, or paraffin hydrocarbons; (2) cyclic, aryl, or ring hydrocarbons; (3) heterocyclic hydrocarbons.

In the aliphatic series, the fundamental or basic compound is methane, CH_4. If one of the hydrogen atoms should be removed from this molecule, the group, methyl, $—CH_3$ remains. Two such groups can unite to form a new molecule, ethane, $H_3C \cdot CH_3$, or, in short, C_2H_6. If a hydrogen atom is removed from ethane, the ethyl group $H_3C \cdot CH_2$— may again be combined with a methyl group to form propane, $H_3C \cdot CH_2 \cdot CH_3$, or C_3H_8. A *general* formula for the methane series of hydrocarbons is C_nH_{2n+2}, in which n is the number of carbon atoms present. They are found in petroleum and natural gas, hence the name "paraffin" sometimes given to the series. More than a hundred of them have been identified and catalogued. The waxy material we call "paraffine" is in this class. Its molecule contains twenty to thirty carbon atoms.

The third member of the methane series, propane, is the principal constituent of the bottled gas sold for cooking and heating purposes in rural areas. The fourth member is butane, C_4H_{10}, which plays an all-important part in aviation gasoline and in synthetic rubber. Hexane, C_6H_{14}, heptane, C_7H_{16}, and octane, C_8H_{18}, form the basic compounds of ordinary motor gasolines, but by themselves have poor anti-knock properties, and must be blended with organics of a different type.

If two hydrogen atoms are removed from the methane molecule, the methylene *group*, $=CH_2$ results. Two such groups unite to form ethylene, $H_2C=CH_2$, which is the fundamental or basic member of the olefin series of hydrocarbons. The olefines are not found in petroleum or natural gas, but are easily produced therefrom by heating the paraffins to a high temperature. This is called "cracking." A dehydrogenation catalyst such as aluminum oxide helps to split hydrogen from the paraffins. Propene, $CH_3—CH=CH_2$, and butene, $CH_3—CH_2—CH=CH_2$, are the next higher members of the olefine series. The general formula for this series is C_nH_{2n}. Like the paraffins, the olefines have the carbon atoms linked together in a long-chain structure.

By the removal of two atoms of carbon from an olefine, a diolefine is formed. The first member of the series is propadiene, $CH_2=C=CH_2$; the second, butadiene, $CH_2=CH—CH=CH_2$. This compound is of great importance in synthetic rubber, for it comprises 75 per cent of the raw material required for tire stock. Nature does not provide it. Its logical chemical genesis is as follows: Butane, $CH_3—CH_2—CH_2—CH_3$, a constituent of natural gas and petroleum, is cracked at a high temperature and loses two atoms of hydrogen to form butene, $CH_3—CH_2—CH=CH_2$; a second cracking to split off two more hydrogen atoms forms butadiene, $CH_2=CH—CH=CH_2$.

A third subdivision of the aliphatic hydrocarbons is the acetylene series. Three atoms of hydrogen removed from methane leave the methylidine group $\equiv CH$, with three free valences. Two such groups combine to form the basic member of the series, acetylene, $HC\equiv CH$. A second member of this series is propine, $CH_3—C\equiv CH$, a third butine, $CH_3—CH_2—C\equiv CH$. The general formula for the series is C_nH_{2n-2}.

The olefines are very reactive compounds, and are important starting materials for the production of many industrial chemicals. The double valence bond between two carbon atoms seems to be under great strain, for these forces of attraction diverge normally at an angle of 109°. Such a double bond is easily ruptured, producing two free valences, one to each carbon atom, ready to attach to atoms or groups in similar reactive condition. The triple bond in the acetylene series is under even greater strain, and the acetylenes are even more reactive than the olefines.

In Chapter I reference was made to compounds that have the same molecular weight and contain the same number of atoms, yet possess quite different chemical properties. Such compounds are called isomers. They are very common among hydrocarbons, and greatly increase the number of different compounds in these series of hydrocarbons. For example, in normal butane, which has the formula CH_3—CH_2—CH_2—CH_3, the carbon atoms are linked together in a long straight chain. Rearrangement of a hydrogen atom forms a different compound, isobutane, CH_3—$\overset{\displaystyle CH_3 \diagdown}{CH}$—$CH_3$, which has very different properties from the normal straight-chain butane. By rearrangement of hydrogen atoms there are three pentanes, five hexanes. The number of possible isomers increases rapidly with the number of carbon atoms present. In the upper members of the series there are millions of possible isomers. Hydrocarbons of the type illustrated above by isobutane are called *branched-chain hydrocarbons*.

A uniform nomenclature is used to designate the individual members of a series, either straight-chain or branched-chain. The names of the hydrocarbons of the paraffin series all end in *-ane;* of the olefine series in *-ene;* of the acetylene series in *-yne* or *-ine*. The root names are the Greek numerals designating the number of carbon atoms in the chain. In the case of branched-chain hydrocarbons, the root is the name of the longest straight-chain group in the compound; and a similar root is chosen for the side-chain and incorporated as a prefix. An Arabic numeral *before the prefix* designates the exact carbon atom of the main chain to which the side-chain is attached. A simple example is 2 methyl butane,

$$CH_3—CH_2—CH_2—CH_3$$
$$|$$
$$CH_3$$

The side-chain methyl group is attached to the second carbon atom of the butane group, this latter being the longest straight-chain in the compound. This system applies equally well to branched-branched chains, the secondary branches being enclosed in parentheses to permit complete designation of nature and position.

The methylene group $=CH_2$ may combine with itself into a series of *ring* compounds, called the *cycloparaffins*. The first two members of the series are:

$$\text{cyclopropane } CH_2 \underset{\diagdown CH_2}{\overset{\diagup CH_2}{\big|}}$$

cyclobutane
$$\begin{array}{c} CH_2\!\!-\!\!CH_2 \\ | \qquad | \\ CH_2\!\!-\!\!CH_2 \end{array}$$

Cyclohexane, which has six such groups *in a ring,* is an important raw material for the production of nylon, one of the ingredients of synthetic rubber, and for many new, laboratory-created commercial products.

Of far greater importance than the cycloparaffines are the aromatic ring hydrocarbons of the benzene series. The simplest member of this series is benzene itself, known commercially as benzol. It is a by-product of the coking of coal, each ton of coal yielding about three gallons of this liquid. The formula for benzene is C_6H_6. The six carbon atoms are chemically identical and are attached to one another by alternating single and double bonds. One atom of hydrogen is linked to each carbon atom. Structurally this can be represented thus:

or simply

Since benzene forms the nucleus of many of the most important organic compounds, the use of a simple regular hexagon without insertion of any symbols for carbon and hydrogen is now universal.

Another light oil derived from the distillation of coal is toluene, a close relative of benzene. Its chemical formula is $C_6H_5CH_3$. A methyl group, CH_3, substitutes for one of the hydrogen atoms of benzene. Toluene is a raw material for many dyes and pharmaceuticals, and for the explosive TNT. Xylene has *two* methyl groups in place of two hydrogen atoms, and is an important thinner and solvent in the lacquer industry, a raw material for dyes and plastics, and a base for aviation gasoline.

Several hundred organic compounds have been found in the thick black tar of the coke ovens. Two of the most important hydrocarbons are naphthalene, $C_{10}H_8$, and anthracene, $C_{14}H_{10}$, which are recovered in relatively pure form. A large number of derivatives, principally dyes, are made from them. Naphthalene is the white flaky solid used in "moth balls." In recent years a derivative of benzene, somewhat more effective, has replaced much of the naphthalene for this purpose, but the household use was never significant when compared with the great quantities of naphthalene used in the dye and synthetic resin industries. Anthracene goes mostly into the production of the best of the light-fast dyes.

Hydrocarbons possessing a ring structure and having other elements with carbon in the ring are called *heterocyclic* hydrocarbons. Nitrogen, sulphur, and oxygen are common substitutes for one or more of the carbon atoms. For example, pyridine, C_5H_5N, is a coal-tar product. Derivatives are found widely in the vegetable kingdom, in dyes, in pharmaceuticals, and in many synthetic products.

The several groups of hydrocarbons described above may be regarded as the fundamental or parent materials for the vast number of possible organic compounds. Any individual organic compound is merely one of the above hydrocarbons with one or more of its hydrogen atoms replaced by another element or by an organic group. When these substitutions determine the chemical nature of the resulting compound, they are called *functional* groups. ("Replacing the hydrogen atoms" is really a figure of speech; the actual reactions of synthesis are not so simple as that—though even direct replacement is not often very easy.)

Only a selected few of the many groups of organic compounds derived from the basic ones can be discussed here. To include all would require several volumes. A complete compendium of the known organic compounds would fill several bookshelves. The most important groups are:

Halogen Compounds. The elements fluorine, chlorine, bromine, and iodine have many characteristics in common and are called *halogens* (that is, "producers of salt"). They readily combine with hydrocarbons to form organic haloids. Chlorine is most used because it is easily obtainable and very cheap. It can react with methane, replacing from one to all four of the hydrogen atoms: monochlormethane, CH_3Cl; dichlormethane, CH_2Cl_2; trichlormethane, $CHCl_3$; tetrachlormethane, CCl_4, often called carbon tetrachloride. This last is an ingredient of many household cleaning fluids, and is used in a common type of fire extinguisher. Methane is highly inflammable, but the inflammability of its chlorinated forms decreases as the chlorine content increases. All members of the aliphatic series may be chlorinated; they form important intermediates in many processes. The chlorinated derivatives of ethylene and acetylene are industrial solvents, and are used in the dry-cleaning industry, and for cleaning delicate machine parts of oil.

Chlorinated benzene, C_6H_5Cl, is an important dye intermediate. There are three possible dichlorbenzenes, depending on which carbon atoms the chlorine atoms attach themselves to. It is customary to number the carbon atoms in the benzene ring by starting with 1 at the top of the hexagon, and proceeding around the ring clockwise. Orthodichlorbenzene has its two chlorine atoms in positions 1 and 2; metadichlorbenzene in positions 1 and 3; paradichlorbenzene in positions 1 and 4. The three compounds have very different properties. The para compound repels and poisons insects, especially moths (this is the benzene derivative that has replaced naphthalene). It is commonly called paradichlor, and also sold under many trade names. It evaporates slowly in the air, and must be replenished from time to time.

Alcohols. When one or more of the hydrogen atoms of a hydrocarbon are replaced by hydroxyl groups, —OH, an alcohol results. The more common alcohols contain only one hydroxyl group. They take the name of the basic hydrocarbon with the suffix *-ol*. The simplest formula is methanol, CH_3OH, long called wood alcohol, for it was formerly obtained by the distillation of wood. Today it is made from coke and steam. It is an important solvent, and to some extent is used in antifreeze.

Ethanol, CH_3CH_2OH, or C_2H_5OH, which is the alcohol in beverages, results from the fermentation of sugar. Large quantities are also made synthetically from ethylene, which in turn is made by cracking petroleum residues. While millions of gallons are used for antifreeze, it is also important as a solvent, and even greater quantities are used to make synthetic rubber. There are two propanols, the normal, $CH_3CH_2CH_2OH$, and the isopropanol, $CH_3CHOHCH_3$. Alcohol derivatives of the higher members of the paraffin series of hydrocarbons have many such isomers: four butanols, eight pentanols, etc.

The alcohols containing *two* hydroxyl groups are called glycols. Ethylene glycol, $HOCH_2CH_2OH$, forms about 95 per cent of a well known brand of antifreeze which does not boil away when the engine becomes overheated. Methanol and ethanol have lower boiling points than water, and hence will boil out of a water mixture, leaving the radiator without protective antifreeze. Ethylene glycol is also an important raw material in explosive manufacture, and many of its derivatives are solvents and modifying agents in coatings.

Alcohols containing *three* hydroxyl groups are called glycerols. The most common is glycerine, $CH_2OHCHOHCH_2OH$. The principal supply is obtained from animal fats and vegetable oils as a by-product of soap manufacture. Many tons are consumed in the explosives and the coating industries. The tobacco industry uses it to keep tobacco moist, for it has great affinity for water.

Ethers are compounds formed of two parent hydrocarbon groups joined to an atom of oxygen, as in the common anesthetic, ethyl ether, C_2H_5—O—C_2H_5. Its manufacture is quite simple. Very pure alcohol is mixed with strong sulphuric acid and heated. Sulphuric acid has a strong affinity for water, which it holds with great tenacity. The ether, which is quite volatile, distills off. The chemical reaction is

$$2\ C_2H_5OH = (C_2H_5)_2O + H_2O$$

The sulphuric acid does not actually enter into the product, and may be concentrated for reuse. In some of the complex ethers the hydrocarbon groups may be different members of the series, as for example, methyl-ethyl ether, CH_3—O—C_2H_5.

Aldehydes are characterized by the substitution of the group —CHO. If methyl alcohol and oxygen are caused to react under suitable conditions, formaldehyde is formed:

$$2 \ CH_3OH + O_2 = 2 \ HCHO + 2 \ H_2O$$

Acetaldehyde is CH_3CHO.

These compounds are extremely reactive, for they possess a double bond in the functional group H

—C̈=O which ruptures easily and permits a union with active free atoms or chemical groups. The aldehydes are widely used in chemical synthesis and in plastics.

Organic Acids contain the carboxyl group —COOH. Formic acid, the active principle in the sting of the bee, the wasp and the ant, is HCOOH. Vinegar contains acetic acid, CH_3COOH. Butyric acid, $CH_3CH_2CH_2COOH$, gives the characteristic odor to rancid butter. From benzene comes benzoic acid, C_6H_5COOH, an important antiseptic and preservative. These are true acids, the hydrogen of the functional group being replaceable by a metal; but compared to the mineral acids they are very weak. The organic acids are often called carboxylic acids.

There are organic acids of great commercial importance that contain two or more carboxyl groups. These polybasic acids are intermediates in the dye and synthetic resin industries, as for example, ortho-benzene-dicarboxylic acid, commercially called phthalic acid, $HOOCC_6H_4COOH$.

Amines and Amino Acids. The amino group —NH_2 may substitute for a hydrogen atom in a hydrocarbon to form an amide. A simple primary amide is methylamine, CH_3NH_2; a secondary one is dimethylamine, $(CH_3)_2NH$; a tertiary, trimethylamine, $(CH_3)_3N$. Commercially the most important amine is aniline, $C_6H_5NH_2$, an intermediate for the so-called coal-tar dyes and pharmaceuticals. It is consumed in large quantities in the rub-

ber industry. The corresponding toluene amide, which is tolui-
dine, $CH_3C_6H_4NH_2$, is a starting point for dyes and pharmaceuticals.

Nitrogen is essential to living plants and animals, in the form
of amines, more abundantly as amino acids. A large number of
these organic acids containing the amine group combine in a most
complex manner to form albumens and proteins; these with starch
make up the cell structure of plants, which animals then eat. The
albumens and proteins have very large molecules, some with molecular weights of more than 100,000. The atoms involved are of
relatively light weights, and so there must be many hundred atoms
in one of these molecules. This will be further discussed later.

In inorganic chemistry metals and bases combine with acids to
form salts, which make up most of the solid crust of the earth. The
combination of organic hydrocarbons and alcohols with acids is
quite analogous; the organic compounds are called *esters.* Just as
the mineral world is composed largely of salts, the living world
is composed largely of esters. The esters do not form as readily as
salts. The reactions producing them are much slower, and rarely
use up the reagents.

The aromatic hydrocarbons form a number of commercially
important esters with mineral acids. Benzene will combine directly with very strong sulphuric acid, if plenty of the latter is used,
to form benzene sulphonate:
$$C_6H_6 + H_2SO_4 = C_6H_5HSO_3 + H_2O$$
This is the starting point for many benzene derivatives. Naphthalene forms a large number of sulphonates which are intermediates
in the coal-tar dye industry.

The nitric acid esters of the hydrocarbons play a most important part in modern explosives. The nitroparaffines are comparatively new, for a safe method of producing them has been developed
only recently; the vapors of nitric acid and of the hydrocarbon are
caused to react, producing the nitro compound. Their principal
use is as solvents and softening agents in coatings.

Aromatic hydrocarbons are nitrated in large quantity, for the
high explosive TNT, or trinitrotoluene, $CH_3C_6H_2(NO_2)_3$, is
most important for shells and bombs. In the production of nitro-

aromatics, a simple reaction with nitric acid is not possible. A mixture of concentrated nitric and sulphuric acids must be used. The sulphuric acid takes up the water produced by the union of the nitric acid and the hydrocarbon, permitting the reaction to proceed to complete utilization of the hydrocarbon.

Aniline is the starting compound for a large number of dyes, and must be produced synthetically, for the amount found in coal tar is far too little for this large industry. In its production benzene is first converted to mononitrobenzene, $C_6H_5NO_2$, by agitating it in mixed nitricsulphuric acid:

$$C_6H_6 + HNO_3 = C_6H_5NO_2 + H_2O$$

The nitrobenzene is then charged into a reduction vessel with iron borings and a little hydrochloric acid. The hydrochloric acid reacting with the iron produces hydrogen, which reduces the nitrobenzene to aniline:

$$C_6H_5NO_2 + 3 H_2 = C_6H_5NH_2 + 2 H_2O$$

This is a typical example of the production of a compound by indirect methods, when it cannot be made by direct combination.

Organic acids and alcohols form esters also. Palmitic acid, $C_{15}H_{31}COOH$, and stearic acid, $C_{17}H_{35}COOH$, and oleic acid, $C_{17}H_{33}COOH$, are found naturally combined with the alcohol, glycerine. Palm oil is the basis of the soap industry; its composition

$$C_{15}H_{31}COOCH_2$$
$$|$$
$$C_{15}H_{31}COOCH$$
$$|$$
$$C_{15}H_{31}COOCH_2$$

Linseed oil is a glyceride of linoleic acid, this latter being an unsaturated compound with two double bonds, which rupture easily and combine with oxygen from the air to form a resinous compound. This is why paint containing linseed oil dries. Chinese tung oil is also a glyceride of an organic acid that contains three double bonds, which gives even faster drying; hence it is preferred for the very quick-drying varnishes.

Esters of glycerine and phthalic acid form resins used in the modern synthetic enamels and varnishes. The production of such resins to replace natural products involves a very important and widely applied principle. Isomers have been defined as compounds of identical composition and molecular weight but different properties. There are also compounds of the same percentage composition but widely different molecular weights. These have the same elements in the same proportions, but some have larger molecules than others. Such compounds are called *polymers,* and the phenomenon of aggregated molecules is called *polymerization.* However, it is not a case of molecules attaching themselves like a swarm of bees, nor is it the snowball type of growth. With the addition of each new molecule, the whole structure undergoes a complete reorganization. This may be represented by a simple example: Three well known commercial products are:

Cyanamide, H_2CN_2

Dicyandiamide, $(H_2CN_2)_2$

Melamine, $(H_2CN_2)_3$

While analysis shows the same percentages of hydrogen, carbon, and nitrogen, the molecular weights are respectively 42, 84, 126. The differences in the structures of the molecules are shown by these structural formulas:

Cyanamide Dicyandiamide Melamine

$$
\begin{array}{ccc}
\text{H}\diagdown & \diagup \text{NHCN} & \text{NH}_2 \\
\quad \text{N—C}\equiv\text{N} & \text{C}\!=\!\text{NH} & | \\
\text{H}\diagup & \diagdown \text{NH}_2 & \text{C}
\end{array}
$$

$$
\begin{array}{c}
\diagup \text{N} \quad \text{N} \diagdown \\
\text{H}_2\text{N—C} \qquad \text{C—NH}_2 \\
\diagdown \text{N} \diagup
\end{array}
$$

Note that with each successive addition of a cyanamide molecule, there is a complete rearrangement of all the atoms in the final compound.

Many commercial products are built up from relatively simple molecules of low molecular weight into polymers with molecular weights of ten, twenty, and even hundreds of thousands. The addition of each new molecule creates a wholly new internal structure, with a new balance of the valence linkages. And at each stage of the aggregation the product takes on new properties. In creating such polymers for commercial purposes, it is necessary to stop the aggregation at just that point at which the desired properties are attained.

The problem of controlling such reactions is one of the most difficult the chemist encounters. It is fundamental in the production of synthetic resins, the molding plastics, and the new types of synthetic rubber. The controls consist of proper timing, temperatures, the degree of acidity or alkalinity of the reacting masses, the presence of catalysts. In the resins for coatings, an aggregation forming a more or less symmetrical molecule is desired. For compounds which must have great elasticity, such as rubber or nylon, growth in long chains, with relatively little bonding to adjacent chains, is desired. The choice of the reagents determines the character of the polymers to a large degree.

Carbohydrates. The sugar in the bowl, the starch in the pudding, and the wood in the dining table are chemically very much alike. They are called carbohydrates, and have six, or a multiple of six, carbon atoms. They also contain hydrogen and oxygen in the ratio of two hydrogen atoms to one of oxygen. This happens to be the same ratio in which hydrogen and oxygen combine to form water, but they are not so combined in these compounds. The carbohydrates are essentially of vegetable origin, and are widely distributed on the face of the world, furnishing an important food for animal and man.

Glucose, $C_6H_{12}O_6$, sometimes called dextrose, and grape sugar, is found in the juices of many sweet fruits and in honey. Chemically it might well be classified as an aldehyde. It usually occurs along with an isomer, fructose. Cane sugar, derived either from the sugar cane or from the sugar beet, has the chemical formula $C_{12}H_{22}O_{11}$, with milk sugar and malt sugar as isomers. When cane sugar is warmed with slightly acidulated water it breaks down into glucose and fructose:

$$C_{12}H_{22}O_{11} \; + \; H_2O \; = \; C_6H_{12}O_6 \; + \; C_6H_{12}O_6$$
cane sugar   glucose   fructose

Fruit juices are readily fermented, the glucose and the fructose being converted into ethyl alcohol (ethanol) by the action of yeast, which may be considered as a vegetable catalyst.

$$C_6H_{12}O_6 = 2\ C_2H_5OH + 2\ CO_2$$

Cane sugar does not itself ferment, and must first be "inverted" to glucose by the process described above.

Starch, $(C_6H_{10}O_5)_n$, is found in the cells of all green plants as microscopic granules of highly organized structure. Actually it is a polymer of $C_6H_{10}O_5$ of an unknown number of molecular aggregations, as is indicated by the subscript n. It is insoluble in cold water, but when boiled it swells up and becomes the well known starch paste. Water has entered the individual molecules. Starch may be converted into glucose by an enzyme (an organic catalyst). This is the mechanism by which corn is converted into alcohol. The ground corn is mixed with a small amount of sprouted grain which contains the enzyme, in a tub of warm water to form the mash:

$$C_6H_{10}O_5 \quad + \quad H_2O \quad = \quad C_6H_{12}O_6$$
$$\text{starch} \qquad\qquad\qquad \text{glucose}$$

Yeast is then added to convert to alcohol.

As a growing plant matures, its starch is transformed into a higher polymer, cellulose, $(C_6H_{10}O_5)_m$, a fibrous material bound together by incrusting substances, sap, gum, and resin. Cellulose is the basis of the paper and rayon industries. It can be nitrated to guncotton, or nitrocellulose, for explosives and celluloid lacquer bases (including nail polish).

Multiple Functions. The few classes of organic compounds in this brief review were all characterized by a single functional substitution—an atom or group of atoms replacing a hydrogen atom. Many organics have two or more such functional substitutions. For example, sour milk is the result of the fermentation of milk sugar to lactic acid, $CH_3CHOHCOOH$. It has both the hydroxyl of an alcohol and the carboxyl of an organic acid, so that the problem of classifying the result is simple; for fermented milk sugar possesses a strongly acid character, and is placed in a subclassification of hydroxy-organic acids. This is usually the case in multiple substitutions; the qualities of one of the functional groups will predominate.

There are compounds in which aromatic rings are joined to aliphatic chains, and aliphatic chains in which aromatic rings have been substituted. These are classified in one or the other series according to their dominant characteristic.

There are hundreds of thousands of well defined organic compounds about which a great deal is known. Thousands of new ones are developed each year in university and private laboratories. For many of these compounds there is no immediate application; but they are real materials, not merely textbook theoretical possibilities, and practical applications for some of them will undoubtedly appear later. This has happened many times in the past. As knowledge increases, man perceives new relationships, new meanings, and ultimately new uses. Dye plants, pharmaceutical producers, plastics manufacturers now produce almost a billion dollars' worth a year of compounds which were unknown only a few decades ago. The chemical industry is in its infancy; a million more products await discovery!

CHAPTER V

FAIRY TALES AND HARD FACTS

If I entered a high-class restaurant in any large city and ordered a sirloin steak, and a platter containing a lump of Texas ranch soil was set before me, it would just about parallel the widely advertised story that a certain brand of hosiery is coal, air, and water.

The Texas soil produces grass, and a great cattle industry feeds and fattens steers on that grass. A gigantic transportation system hauls the steers to a packing house, where they are slaughtered, cut up, and converted into many kinds of food and by-products. One of these, a side of beef, is transported to a cold-storage plant, from which it ultimately goes to a retailer, who cuts and sorts it further, and sells parts of it to my restaurant. Many millions of dollars have been invested in the tools and equipment required to place that steak before me. An army of highly trained men and many coordinated services have been utilized. The little patch of Texas soil is forgotten in this vast industrial complexity.

The same thing is true of the coal, air, and water. They are insignificant in the history of a pair of stockings, in comparison with the millions of dollars and years of effort spent on research, the millions in capital invested in plants that convert these raw materials, transform them into intermediates, then into still more complex substances, polymerize these, and extrude the final material, which then must be made into yarn, and be sent to the spinners and knitters, the dyers and finishers. Thousands of highly trained engineers and technicians have studied and labored to bring all this about.

Is not this all more interesting and romantic than the rhetorical hocus-pocus whereby the public is led to believe that marvelous products just slip out of some chemist's magical sleeve?

For example, scarcely one person in a hundred ever thinks of the importance of the mineral acids in the national life. Yet, it has often been said, a nation's standard of living can be gauged by its annual production of sulphuric acid.

In 1941 the United States produced more than seven million tons of this all-important acid, far more than any other country in the world. The largest consumer is the fertilizer industry, though sulphuric acid is not a plant food, and in many cases is a detriment and its residual influences in the fertilizer on crop growth must be corrected. The second largest consumer is the petroleum industry, but no sulphuric acid is found in any commercial product of the oil industry. Explosives, both commercial and military, require enormous quantities of sulphuric acid, but none of it is in any finished explosive. The steel industry uses more than half a million tons of it annually to remove mill scale, or oxide coating, from sheet steel before it is tinned or galvanized, or polished. Yet there is no sulphuric acid in the steel as shipped. Copper, zinc, rayon, photographic film, textiles, pigments and dry colors, plastics—all require sulphuric acid as an auxiliary reagent in the course of their manufacture; but only insignificant amounts remain in the finished products. Only 10 per cent of all the sulphuric acid production goes into sulphate salts and sulphonate esters in which its functional properties are of primary importance.

More than a hundred million dollars is invested in the sulphuric acid industry. Without a cheap and abundant supply of the acid our civilization, with its conveniences and comforts, could not exist. In the recent awakening of China and India sulphuric acid plants were among the very first of the new industrial units.

Sulphuric acid, H_2SO_4, as marketed, is a heavy oily colorless liquid. The more common commercial grades are: chamber acid, containing 75 per cent sulphuric acid; oil of vitriol, containing 92 per cent; 98 per cent; and the oleums containing up to 40 per cent free sulphur trioxide.

For the purpose of understanding its methods of production, this acid may be thought of as a combination of sulphur trioxide, SO_3, and water. Since water, and oxygen from the atmosphere, are abundant, the important raw material is the sulphur. The principal ores of copper, lead, and zinc (sulphides) contain sulphur. The sulphur must be removed before the ores can be converted into metals, and this is accomplished by heating them in air (roasting). The sulphur burns to sulphur dioxide, SO_2, and the metal constituent is converted to oxide. The sulphur dioxide is a pungent gas (burning sulphur candles give it off) that is sent to the sulphuric acid plant for further conversion to acid. The metal oxides go to the metal furnaces.

Along with the sulphide ores is found a disulphide of iron, iron pyrites, FeS_2. This also is an important source of sulphur for acid making. It is roasted for the production of sulphur dioxide, and the iron oxide residue goes to the blast furnace for the production of pig iron. About one-third of the sulphuric acid produced in the United States is a by-product of smelter operations.

Close to the Gulf of Mexico in the states of Louisiana and Texas are scattered "salt domes"—huge blocks of rock salt in the form of a crude sugar loaf, a thousand feet or more below the surface of the earth. Petroleum is frequently found around their margins, and oil prospectors have located most of the known salt domes. The rock salt is crowned with a thick layer of gypsum (calcium sulphate), and in a few of the domes the gypsum contains rather pure sulphur in quantity.

The sulphur is extracted from these deposits in a very ingenious way. A hole is drilled down to the sulphur-bearing gypsum and lined with steel casing. Two pipes, one inside the other, are then put inside the casing. Hot water, forced down between the casing and the larger pipe, melts the sulphur, which collects as a liquid at the bottom of the drill-hole. Compressed air is sent down the central pipe and lifts the molten sulphur in the space between the inner and outer pipes. The sulphur, mixed with water, is led to large wooden bins, the water runs off, and the sulphur gradually cools and freezes to a solid mass. The wooden sides of the bins are removed, the block of sulphur is broken down by explosives, shoveled into cars, and sent to market. This Gulf sulphur is the raw material for about two-thirds of the sulphuric acid produced

FERTILIZER AND FOOD

The corn on left received 400 pounds of fertilizer per acre; on right, none

RAYON SPINNING UNIT

Automatically extruding, coagulating, washing, bleaching, drying,

in the United States, and much of it is exported to foreign countries.

When sulphur burns in air it produces mostly sulphur dioxide, very little sulphur trioxide. Sulphur trioxide is not stable at high temperatures, and dissociates or decomposes into the dioxide and oxygen. The flame of the burning sulphur is too hot for the production of the trioxide. If the dioxide, mixed with air (oxygen), is passed over a catalyst it will be oxidized to the trioxide with almost 100 per cent efficiency. The catalyst consists of small pellets of vanadium oxide and potassium sulphate, carried on an inert filler. The pellets are supported on perforated trays in a vessel called a converter, and the gases are passed through the mass at a temperature just below red heat. The reactions involved are

$$S + O_2 = SO_2 \text{ (roasting)}$$
$$2\,SO_2 + O_2 = 2\,SO_3 \text{ (converting)}$$

The gases leaving the converter are cooled, and scrubbed in tall towers with sulphuric acid above 92 per cent concentration. The sulphur trioxide dissolves only very slowly in water, but is taken up with great avidity by strong sulphuric acid. Water is added to maintain the desired concentration.

Sulphuric acid of 100 per cent concentration will continue to dissolve sulphur trioxide, even as much as 40 per cent of its weight. These exceedingly strong acids are called oleums. They are particularly useful in chemical reactions to absorb water.

Sulphuric is a strong acid and has a relatively high boiling point. It sets many other acids free from their salts, allowing them to be distilled off without itself being in danger of vaporizing. Acetic acid, for example, can be produced from calcium acetate; hydrochloric acid from sodium chloride; hydrofluoric acid from fluorspar; and oxalic acid from calcium oxalate—all by heating the respective salt with sulphuric acid, and condensing the more volatile acid from the vapors. The reaction for hydrochloric acid is

$$2\,NaCl \quad + \quad H_2SO_4 \quad = \quad 2\,HCl \quad + \quad Na_2SO_4$$

| salt | sulphuric acid | hydrochloric acid | sodium sulphate |

This reaction takes place in a rotary furnace fired by oil or gas. The salt and sulphuric acid, in proper proportions, are fed into the cooler end; the sodium sulphate passes out at the hot end. The gases from the burning fuel carry off the hydrochloric acid vapor, and are drawn into tall towers down which water is sprayed. This dissolves out the acid, which is recovered from the bottom of the tower as a water solution. The commercial product sold under the name of muriatic acid contains about 30 per cent hydrochloric acid.

For a long time nitric acid was made from Chilean nitrate (nitrate of soda), $NaNO_3$, by heating in iron pots with sulphuric acid. This method is now obsolete. The modern way is to mix ammonia and air and burn the mixture in a tightly closed vessel in the interstices of a platinum-gauze catalyst. The whole operation includes several chemical steps, and the chain of apparatus is kept under a pressure of about 100 pounds per square inch. The ammonia, which comes in liquid form under pressure, is first vaporized and mixed with compressed air in the proportion of about ten volumes of air to one volume of ammonia. This mixture is passed through the red-hot platinum gauze, which brings about the reaction:

$$4\,NH_3 \;+\; 5\,O_2 \;=\; 4\,NO \;+\; 6\,H_2O$$

ammonia		nitric	water
		oxide	(steam)

The air carries five parts of nitrogen to one part oxygen, but its nitrogen takes no part in these reactions. The combustion of the ammonia in the gauze maintains this at the necessary high temperature; it is kindled on starting with a small gas flame.

The hot gases from the oxidation converter are cooled, and during the cooling the nitric oxide reacts with more air to form nitrogen peroxide:

$$4\,NO + 2\,O_2 = 2\,N_2O_4$$

nitrogen
peroxide

This is then scrubbed with water to form nitric acid:

$$2\,N_2O_4 + O_2 + 2\,H_2O = 4\,HNO_3$$

nitric
acid

The air originally mixed with the ammonia supplies the oxygen for all the reactions.

The acid produced by this process is only of 60 per cent strength, not strong enough for the many uses in the explosives and synthetic organic industries. It is not possible to concentrate it by boiling off water, for the acid would vaporize also. A more complicated concentrating system had to be devised. The weak nitric acid is mixed with four or five times its weight of sulphuric acid of 85 per cent strength. This holds the water and permits distilling the nitric acid from the mixture. A concentrated nitric acid is recovered by condensation of the vapors. The sulphuric acid has been diluted in this operation and is sent to its concentrator and, after restoration to its original strength, can be used over and over.

The production of alkali is just as good a gauge of a nation's standard of living as the production of sulphuric acid. By alkali we mean sodium carbonate, or soda ash, Na_2CO_3, and sodium hydroxide, or caustic soda, NaOH. The corresponding potassium compounds might also be included, but their tonnage is relatively small as compared with that of the sodium bases. In 1941 the United States consumed more than three and a half million tons of soda ash, of which about 20 per cent was converted into caustic soda. Caustic soda, in addition was produced to the extent of 650,000 tons by a wholly different process. Over two hundred million dollars is invested in the alkali industry, and large as it was, the demands for war purposes required the construction of much additional plant.

Glass is a combination of soda, lime, and silica, and the glass industry consumes over a million tons of soda ash a year. Soaps and cleaning agents use 10 per cent of the ash production (also a large quantity of caustic soda). Baking soda takes a hundred and fifty thousand tons of soda ash in a year. The aluminum industry is dependent on it for the purification of its ores. The better qualities of pulp and paper, and textile finishing, consume over two hundred thousand tons annually.

The makers of rayon and cellulose film are the largest consumers of caustic soda. Soap, petroleum refining, organic chemicals, pulp, paper, mercerizing, rubber reclaiming all are important users of this strong alkali.

A small amount of soda ash is recovered from natural deposits in the desert areas of the Far West; but this soda is less pure than that manufactured, and finds only limited local use. All other ash and caustic are produced from common salt, sodium chloride. Sodium and chlorine have strong mutual affinities, and it is not easy to separate them. Two methods are in common use throughout the world. For the production of soda ash, the Solvay process, developed in Belgium, has displaced all other methods for seventy-five years.

The raw material is common salt dissolved in water; the solution is commonly referred to as brine. This solution is usually prepared by drilling into a salt deposit and pumping fresh water down to the salt strata. The salt dissolves underground to a saturated brine which is lifted to the surface and pumped to the soda plant. There it runs into a tall tower, and ammonia gas under pressure is bubbled through it until the brine will absorb no more. This ammoniated brine is next pumped to another tall tower, and carbon dioxide gas, obtained from sources described later, is bubbled through it. In the presence of the ammonia and carbon dioxide, the salt in the brine is decomposed, and sodium bicarbonate, $NaHCO_3$, and ammonium chloride, NH_4Cl, are formed. The bicarbonate separates out as a fine crystal, and the ammonium chloride remains in solution. The bicarbonate crystals go to a low-temperature calcining furnace in which some of the carbon dioxide is driven off, leaving soda ash, Na_2CO_3.

The ammonia is recovered by adding slaked lime to the solution of ammonium chloride and feeding the mixture down a tall column, heated by steam. The lime releases the ammonia, which passes out at the top as a gas, and forms calcium chloride, $CaCl_2$, that runs out the bottom as a solution. The calcium chloride, which may be recovered by evaporating off the water, has a limited market in the refrigeration industry, for snow melting, for road surfacing to hold down dust; but the quantity produced by the Solvay plants is far greater than the market can absorb, and most of it goes to waste.

The lime used for the recovery of the ammonia is made from

limestone, $CaCO_3$, by burning the stone in a kiln to drive off the carbon dioxide. This carbon dioxide is recovered from the kiln gases and is added to that obtained from the ash calcining furnaces, and used to saturate the ammoniated brine. The reactions involved in the several steps:

(1) $$NaCl + NH_3 = (no\ chemical\ reaction)$$
salt   ammonia   ammoniated brine

(2) $$NaCl + NH_3 + CO_2 + H_2O = NaHCO_3 + NH_4Cl$$
ammoniated brine   bicarbonate   ammonium
chloride

(3) $$NaHCO_3 = Na_2CO_3 + CO_2 + H_2O$$
soda ash

The carbon dioxide set free in step (3) is returned to step (2).

(4) $$2\ NH_4Cl + Ca(OH)_2 = 2\ NH_3 + CaCl_2 + 2\ H_2O$$
The ammonia set free in step (4) is returned to step (1).

(5) $$CaCO_3 = CaO + CO_2$$
(6) $$CaO + H_2O = Ca(OH)_2$$

The lime produced in step (5) is slaked with water, step (6), and returned to step (4). The carbon dioxide from step (5) is returned to step (2).

This is an excellent example of how the chemist is forced to use indirect methods to accomplish a desired end. Carbonic acid is too weak to displace hydrochloric acid from sodium chloride. Through the use of ammonia as an auxiliary the desired products are obtained. A study of the reactions above shows that the only raw materials actually consumed in this cycle are salt and limestone. The products are soda ash and calcium chloride, though the latter has little commercial use in comparison with the production. All the reactions except the burning of the limestone and the calcining of the sodium bicarbonate are carried out in water solutions and in a continuous process. Fuel is required for the burning of the lime and the production of steam for the calciners and the ammonia still. Power is required for pumping and gas compression. The process is very efficient, and produces a soda ash of exceptional purity.

Sodium hydroxide, or caustic soda, is easily prepared from soda ash, and calcium hydroxide, or slaked lime. The ash is dissolved in water and the solution is treated with slaked lime. Calcium carbonate is formed according to the equation:

$$Na_2CO_3 + Ca(OH)_2 = 2\,NaOH + CaCO_3$$

It is not soluble in water and settles out of the sodium hydroxide solution. The caustic solution is sent to steamheated evaporators which concentrate it to a 50–55 per cent solution, in which form it is often marketed. If further concentration is desired, this strong solution is sent to fusion pots, fired by gas or oil, and the remainder of the water is driven off. The melted caustic from the pots is cast into sheet-iron drums, and left to cool and solidify. It is sometimes flaked by running the molten caustic over a water-cooled wheel, and scraping the thin solidified sheet off with a knife.

About half the caustic soda used in the United States is made by an entirely different process. A direct electric current passing through a solution of an inorganic salt will decompose the salt. The acid collects around the anode (where the current comes in), and the metallic constituent collects around the cathode (where the current leaves). This phenomenon is called *electrolytic decomposition*, or simply *electrolysis*.

If the salt solution is sodium chloride in water, chlorine will appear at the anode, and sodium at the cathode. But metallic sodium reacts with water and forms sodium hydroxide and hydrogen gas. In short, chlorine gas comes off at the anode, and caustic soda forms around the cathode; the hydrogen gas also comes off the cathode. The anode is of graphite, which is not attacked by chlorine; the cathode is of sheet iron, which is inert to caustic. To keep the caustic solution from coming into contact with the anode and the chlorine freed there, a porous diaphragm of asbestos paper or cloth separates the anode compartment from the cathode compartment. Outlets in the top of the cell, one in each compartment, must be provided to take away the chlorine and the hydrogen in separate gas streams. The over-all reaction taking place in the caustic cell might be written:

$$2\,NaCl + 2\,H_2O \;=\; \underset{\substack{\text{anode}\\\text{product}}}{Cl_2} \;+\; \underset{\substack{\text{cathode products}}}{H_2 \;+\; 2\,NaOH}$$

The chlorine gas is collected in a pipe system and sent to drying towers where all moisture (water vapor) is removed by washing with strong sulphuric acid. It is then compressed, cooled, and liquefied. At summer temperatures the pressure necessary to maintain the liquid state is approximately 150 pounds per square inch, and storage and shipping containers must be strong enough to resist such pressure. If all water is removed, liquid chlorine does not attack iron or steel.

Production of caustic soda by electrolysis costs more than that by the ammonia-soda process. However, there is a by-product credit in the chlorine, and so long as this can be sold above a certain minimum price, the electrolytic caustic is competitive. In recent years, consumption of chlorine has increased, partly for water purification, but mostly for bleaching and the production of synthetics. In war the consumption of chlorine is enormous. Drastic curtailment of civilian use does not free enough to meet military demands. Production of chlorine outside the alkali industry is almost nil, and research has been active for years to develop a process that will increase the supply of chlorine without burdening industry with an excess of alkali.

The production of such chemicals as mineral acids, alkali, and chlorine is not glamorous or romantic. It is simply all-important. Without these heavy chemicals there would be no newspapers, no soap, no aniline dyes or synthetic drugs, in fact very few of the things now regarded as absolute necessities. There are many basic materials of like importance never referred to in the public press.

"Coal-tar dyes" are dyestuffs from coal, as distinguished from those of vegetable origin. Vegetable dyes are very old: the first dye from coal was made by William Henry Perkin, an Englishman, in 1856. Indigo was once obtained from the indigo plant, which grows in tropical countries; only synthetic indigo is used now. Alizarin, a widely used red dye, once came from the European madder plant; now only from a coal-tar constituent. The chemist is ever in competition with nature, and he often wins the contest.

There are no dyes as such in coal, or in coal tar. But the raw materials for dyes, pharmaceuticals, and plastics are produced in the course of making coke from coal. Other by-products of this operation enter into the synthesis of rubber, into explosives, even into a substitute for sugar—saccharin.

When certain varieties of bituminous coal are heated to a high temperature in a closed retort (air being carefully excluded) the coal fuses, evolves a large quantity of gas and vapor, and leaves in the retort a hard porous mass, called coke, which consists of carbon retaining whatever ash there was in the coal. About one-third of the coal becomes gas and vapor, two-thirds coke. Coke is a valuable fuel and reducing agent in metallurgy, because it does not fuse at even the highest temperatures of the electric furnace, while bituminous coal in the raw state melts together in the tall shafts of smelting furnaces and blocks the passage of gas.

The hot gas evolved in the coke ovens is collected and cooled by direct contact with water in cooling towers; tar condenses from it, and separates from the cooling water in settling pits.

The cooled gas is washed in scrubbing towers with a light tar-oil that dissolves certain hydrocarbons out of it. The gas is then led to the ammonia recovery unit, where its ammonia content is absorbed by sulphuric acid. (Coal contains nitrogen, and when coal is distilled, a part of this nitrogen is evolved as ammonia, some being caught in the first cooling waters, and the rest in the sulphuric acid scrubber.) If the gas is sold into a city distribution system, it requires further purification to remove sulphur; this is either washed out with a solution of sodium carbonate, or caught in filter boxes charged with oxide of iron. If the gas is used in a steel mill complete sulphur removal is not so necessary.

Returning to the oil scrubber, the oil, saturated with light oils extracted from the vapors, is distilled, and the hydrocarbons driven off are condensed to *light oil*. The scrubbing oil is cooled and returned to the system for another washing cycle.

From a ton of coal there are recovered:

     1,300 pounds of coke
         3 gallons of light oil
        10 gallons of tar
         5 pounds of ammonia
    10,000 cubic feet of gas

A modern coke plant is very interesting. It consists of one or more batteries, each comprising a parallel series of chambers of firebrick, 30 feet long, 14 to 20 inches wide, and 10 to 12 feet high. Separating the chambers, and built into the partition walls, are heating flues in which gas is burned to heat the oven and its charge of coal to temperatures of nearly 2000° Fahrenheit. The coal is put in through openings in the roof and leveled across the oven by a machine scraper. When the coking operation is over, doors at each end of the oven are raised, and a mechanical pusher slides out the red-hot block of coke. The coke falls into a receiving car where it is quenched with water or steam, so that it does not take fire and burn. Some of the gas made in the oven is used to heat it; but if there is a demand in the neighborhood for city gas the heating is done with a less valuable manufactured gas.

Coke ovens are operated for the production of coke, the value of which covers the cost of the coal. The several by-products take care of the cost of operation, including interest and amortization, and some additional profit. The coking industry of the United States represents an investment of nearly a billion dollars.

The chemical industry is particularly interested in three by-products of the coke oven; light oil, tar, and ammonia. The light oil contains benzene, C_6H_6, toluene, C_7H_8, several xylenes, C_8H_{10}, and small amounts of even more complex hydrocarbons. These valuable compounds can be separated in a high state of purity by distillation. From the pure benzene comes aniline, $C_6H_5NH_2$. It is the starting point for many dyes, pharmaceuticals, photographic developers. Phenol, C_6H_5OH, although found in coal tar, is used in such large amounts that additional quantities must be made from benzene. From toluene come many dye intermediates, explosives, perfumes, and pharmaceuticals. The xylenes are used in the production of certain special dyes. When market conditions do not warrant the expensive separations, the crude light oil is often blended with gasoline for motor fuel. It has excellent anti-knock qualities, which compensate for its higher price.

More than two hundred different compounds have been found in coal tar, but only a few of them are actually separated on a commercial scale. Most of the 750,000,000 gallons of tar produced annually is burned as fuel in the steel furnaces. It has about the same heating power as petroleum oil, and does not contain sulphur. The commercial processing of tar is largely a question of economics, and the operations are adjusted to the demands for the more important constituents.

Tar is put into a still and slowly heated. Any water it contains distills off. As the temperature of the still rises, a light oil, not unlike that recovered from the gas, vaporizes. This is condensed and added to the light oil extracted from the gas. When the temperature of the vapor leaving the still has reached 335° Fahrenheit, the condenser discharge is turned into another receiver, and the oil which vaporizes up to 450° is collected as *middle oil*. This carries phenol, C_6H_5OH, cresol, $C_6H_4CH_3OH$, xylenol, $C_8H_3(CH_3)_2OH$, and naphthalene, $C_{10}H_8$. The mixed phenols, cresols, and xylenols are alcohols rather than acids, but they are known as tar acids throughout the tar industry. They are recovered from the middle oil by repeated addition of small batches of caustic soda solution, with which they combine, separating from the remaining oils. Naphthalene, which comes out as crystal when the middle oil is cooled, is pressed into cakes (the pressure removing any entrained oil). It is usually marketed as crude naphthalene, but can be refined by distillation. It is used not only as a moth repellent, but as the source of a surprising number of dyes and perfumes.

As the still temperature rises above 450° Fahrenheit the condensate is shifted to another receiver in order to recover *heavy creosote oil*, which is run to a top temperature of 525°. This is the creosote oil of commerce, used to preserve wood, piling, telephone poles, railway ties, and mine timbers; its effectiveness lies in its content of tar acids, chiefly cresols and xylenols.

At still temperatures between 525° and 750° Fahrenheit *anthracene oil* distills over. Anthracene, $C_{14}H_{10}$, another important dye intermediate, is obtained in crystal form when this oil fraction is cooled to a low temperature. The residue left behind in the still, after removal of the anthracene oil, is *pitch*. This is a mixture of very heavy hydrocarbons and carbon.

It would be an accident if the commercial demands for all the products of the tar still were in balance with the yields. The tar distiller has had to conduct his operations so as to dispose of excess production of any one or more products in a field in which there is wide tolerance in specifications. Road tars permit such a disposition. The oils and pitch may be blended to produce light to heavy road tars. On the other hand the roofing tars and waterproofing compounds, and the tar compositions used for impregnating paper and felt (roofing or tar paper), are mixed to more exact specifications. The hard pitch is used in the production of electrodes for electric furnaces. Much of it is coked in ovens, to form coke. This is very valuable in the electrodes for making aluminum, since it contains no ash.

Many natural products were formed by chemical reactions deep in the earth under conditions of high pressure and high temperature. The dense vegetation of the Carboniferous period of the earth's history was consolidated into coal beds under heavy layers of sediment—that is, at high pressure—and at temperatures higher than normal. These factors converted the woody fibers into the dense coal. Many valuable ore deposits are concentrations of mineral that was previously taken into solution at very high temperatures and under enormous pressure. The chemist and the chemical engineer are now cooperating to apply these factors, and are conducting large-scale production at pressures as high as 15,-000 pounds per square inch, and at temperatures approaching redness.

Ammonia, NH_3, is now made from the elements hydrogen and nitrogen in every industrialized country in the world, to the extent of more than four million tons a year. The vastly increased demand for explosives—that is, for nitric acid—could only be met by synthetic production. The ammonia plants operate at pressures of 1,500 to 15,000 pounds per square inch (mostly 8,000 to 10,000), depending on which of several developed methods is used.

The plastics industry uses large quantities of formaldehyde, $HCHO$, most of which is made from methanol, CH_3OH. Military explosives also require large quantities of methanol for particularly powerful bursting charges. By the old process of distilling wood (a cord of hardwood yields only four to five gallons), it would be impossible to meet more than a very small fraction of the demand. High-pressure technique makes it possible to produce methanol in any quantity from coke and steam, or natural gas and steam.

When steam is blown through a bed of red-hot coke, water gas (a mixture of carbon monoxide, CO, and hydrogen) is produced. A mixture of natural gas and steam, heated to redness, gives the same product. In either case, the mixture is adjusted to contain one volume of carbon monoxide to two volumes of hydrogen. This is then compressed to around 4,000 pounds per square inch, and passed through a catalyst in a heavy forged-steel tube, something like a large gun barrel. The catalyst contains zinc and chromium oxides. The reaction that takes place is:

$$CO + 2\ H_2 = CH_3OH$$

The issuing gas stream is cooled, and the methanol condensed out, any uncombined gases being returned to the system.

A modern petroleum refinery operates at pressures as high as 1,500 pounds per square inch, and at temperatures approaching 1000° Fahrenheit. The dye industry employs several high-pressure processes—for example, in the production of diphenylamine, $(C_6H_5)_2NH$, the commonly used stabilizer for smokeless powder, and an important intermediate. There are certain reactions that must be carried out not in water but in solvents such as anhydrous ammonia or alcohol. Because of their low boiling points these solvents would evaporate unless kept under pressure in a closed vessel. The problem of finding materials of construction and of designing apparatus that will withstand these high pressures and high temperatures has been solved, and industry no longer hesitates at undertaking production on a large scale in this field.

Aside from the purely metallurgical aspects, the production of aluminum really belongs to heavy chemical industry. Aluminum cannot be easily refined, once in the metallic form, and it has been found simpler to purify all the raw materials entering the process; the resulting metal must therefore be pure. The United States is now about ready to produce more than a million tons of this metal per year, that is five times the prewar output. The principal ore, called bauxite, is a hydrated oxide of aluminum. The natural deposits all contain clay, iron and titanium compounds. A high-grade ore will contain about 60 per cent aluminum oxide, Al_2O_3, nearly 30 per cent water, and the rest undesirable impurities as listed above. If the war program is to be continued for only a few years, much lower-grade ore than the above will have to be utilized. The aluminum oxide (alumina) fed to the reduction cells must not contain more than 0.15 per cent of such impurities as silicon, iron, and titanium. Two tons of purified oxide are required for each ton of metal produced, and the production of these enormous quantities is a major chemical task.

Bauxite is first ground to a coarse powder, which is then digested in a pressure vessel with a solution of caustic soda of about 50 per cent concentration. This dissolves the aluminum hydrate in the ore as sodium aluminate, $Na_2Al_2O_4$, but not the impurities. The strong solution is diluted with water, and the undissolved impurities are filtered out. The clear solution of sodium aluminate is placed in large tanks, a small amount of alumina from a previous batch is added (seeding), and then it is stirred for several days. In the course of time the sodium aluminate, in the now diluted solution, splits into aluminum hydrate, $Al_2O_3 \cdot 3 H_2O$, and caustic soda. This is an interesting example of the chemical phenomenon of a material soluble in a strong solution, and separable in a dilute one, a real chemical reaction taking place in each case. The crystals of hydrated alumina are settled, filtered, and washed to free them from the caustic mother liquor. They are dried, and prepared for the reduction unit by calcining at a very high temperature. The dilute caustic solution is concentrated and used over again.

More than five million tons of bauxite must be treated annually to meet the present aluminum metal schedule; this is chemistry on a large scale. In addition to use for the production of metal alumina, in large quantities, it is fused in electric furnaces for the manufacture of abrasives, particularly for fine grinding wheels which are so important in maintaining the high degree of tolerance imposed on military equipment and aviation engines. Aluminum hydrate is a raw material for paper size, for baking powders and alums, for ceramics and electrical insulators.

Another light metal, magnesium, must also be reduced from pure ore—magnesium chloride, $MgCl_2$. One of the principal sources is sea water, in which about 3.5 per cent of its weight consists of dissolved salts. Magnesium chloride forms one-tenth of the 3.5 per cent, so that a ton of sea water contains about 7 pounds of magnesium chloride. Although this seems to be a very small proportion, the operation to recover it from the ocean is rather simple. The sea water is pumped to large basins, and calcium hydroxide (milk of lime), $Ca(OH)_2$, is added to precipitate the magnesium as hydrate:

$$MgCl_2 + Ca(OH)_2 = Mg(OH)_2 + CaCl_2$$

As magnesium chloride is the only salt present that is precipitated by the milk of lime, it need only be permitted to settle and then be filtered out. It is then dissolved in hydrochloric acid to form pure magnesium chloride, which is dried and is ready for the reduction to metal. An alternate method of conversion to chloride is to heat the magnesium hydroxide with carbon and chlorine. Chlorine is produced in the decomposition of the magnesium chloride in the magnesium cell, and can in this way be returned to the process.

Heat produced by electricity has two unique properties: almost any temperature may be attained, and there are no contaminating gases of combustion. The great importance of the electric furnace in chemistry is exceeded only in the metallurgical industries, where it is supreme. An example is the production of calcium carbide, CaC_2, which requires a temperature higher than can be attained by the combustion of a fuel. Here the starting material is a relatively pure limestone, $CaCO_3$, which is burned in a limekiln to quicklime—calcium oxide, CaO. Coke is mixed with the lime in the proportion of 40 parts of coke to 60 parts of lime, and the mixture smelted in an electric furnace:

$$CaO + 3\,C = CaC_2 + CO$$

The molten carbide is tapped from the furnace, cooled, crushed, and sized for market.

Commercial calcium carbide is approximately 85 per cent pure; it contains some lime that has not been reduced, and the impurities picked up from the ash of the coke, and from the limestone. About two tons of limestone are required to make a ton of carbide. The electric furnace produces about two tons of commercial carbide for each horsepower-year of electric energy supplied (3,300 kilowatt-hours per ton). Individual furnaces rate as high as 30,000 horsepower.

An important use of calcium carbide is as a source of acetylene gas, C_2H_2. To produce this, a carefully designed generator is necessary, for a great deal of heat is set free in the reaction which could cause a violent explosion. The reaction is:

$$CaC_2 + 2\ H_2O = C_2H_2 + Ca(OH)_2$$

The slaked lime is wasted, or is disposed of as agricultural lime. Acetylene is widely used in the welding and cutting of metals, and in the chemical industry for making the acetic acid, CH_3COOH, and acetic anhydride, $(CH_3CO)_2O$, employed in the manufacture of the acetate type of rayon and the cellulose acetate plastics. Acetylene is also a starting material for neoprene—a type of synthetic rubber with superior resistance to oil, which is used for lining hose to convey oil and gasoline. The Germans' whole synthetic rubber program is founded on carbide and acetylene, and they take the latter as their starting material for butadiene.

A large tonnage of carbide is transformed into calcium cyanamide, better known under the trade name of Cyanamid. The carbide, heated in an electric furnace, absorbs nitrogen:

$$CaC_2 + N_2 = CaCN_2 + C$$

The carbon set free in the reaction is a form of graphite. It is not separated, and gives to Cyanamid its characteristic gray color. It contains, in the forms prepared for market, approximately 22 to 24 per cent nitrogen, and is used directly as a fertilizer. Large quantities of Cyanamid are converted into derivatives—for example, calcium cyanide, $Ca(CN)_2$, used in extracting gold and silver from their ores, and in producing insecticides. Cyanide is converted into hydrocyanic acid, HCN, through the use of sulphuric acid. Hydrocyanic acid is one of the most poisonous com-

by fruit, and the seeds of the wild grasses which were the primitive ancestors of our modern grains.

Which came first: animal husbandry or the growing of crops? Crops imply some permanence of residence, for the growth and ripening of the seeds of emmer, wild rye, and millet, which were among the first known grains, require a considerable part of a year.

In various parts of the world graves have been discovered in what must have been primitive man's earliest grain fields. This has given rise to the speculation that agriculture came from the decoration of graves with food and flowers. The seeds thus dropped in newly turned earth sprouted and grew and reproduced themselves—providing food. In time it became customary to bury a corpse in the grain field at seeding time, and if no one had died a living person was sacrificed. Later, an animal carcass replaced the human body in these rites, which persisted well down through history.

However it may have been, as soon as man could rely on his flocks and his grain fields for food and was no longer dependent upon the accidental spoils of the chase, he had leisure to notice and reflect upon the natural phenomena by which his existence was determined. In short, a stable food supply made civilization possible. Even as today.

For thousands of years the soil yielded the harvest without man's knowing why. The earth was plowed, the seeds planted, and in due season the fruit of toil came forth. A lore accumulated, of course, but the scientific knowledge of agriculture began only a hundred years ago, with the German chemist Liebig.

It was long thought that plants drew all their substance from the soil. Many chemists had examined the structure of plants, but they failed to notice that it contains very little mineral matter and almost its whole bulk is water, carbon, hydrogen, and oxygen. The residue of burned plants—the ash—contains all the mineral constituents, and does not exceed 2 per cent of the original weight. (Liebig made the first comprehensive chemical analysis of plant tissues, and found that the principal constituent—forming half the weight—was carbon, which he concluded could come only from the atmosphere.) Hydrogen and oxygen are present in quantity, nearly in the proportion found in water though differently combined. These analyses are of thoroughly dried plant substance (some succulent plants contain more than 90 per cent water in the green state).

Nitrogen is found in all parts of a plant. New green foliage and ripe seeds contain the most; there is little in the woody stems. While the total quantity present is only 1 or 2 per cent of the dry weight of the root, stem, foliage, and seeds, it is a most essential element. Phosphorus also is found in all plants, most prominently in the seeds of grains but also concentrated in the roots; the total quantity is very small. Potassium is an ever-present element, seemingly concentrated in woody stems and in the roots of certain plants. In primitive lands, wood ashes are leached for their potash, to be used in making soap; and it is converted to saltpeter for black-powder manufacture.

The knowledge of plant composition makes possible a rational system of nourishment. Virgin soils contain potash and phosphorus derived from the decomposition of the primary rocks. This weathering goes on continually, slowly replenishing the potash and phosphorus in the soil; but intensive cultivation may carry them away faster than nature can restore them, with resultant impoverishment of the soil.

Carbon comes to plants from the air; yet carbon dioxide, the only form in the atmosphere, is present only to the extent of a few hundredths of 1 per cent. This is produced, along with a large amount of heat, when carbon is burned with air or oxygen. To reverse the reaction and produce carbon and oxygen from carbon dioxide requires that an equal amount of energy be absorbed. In the green leaves of the plant is a complex compound called chlorophyll, of whose constitution and functioning little is known. Under the influence of sunlight chlorophyll absorbs carbon dioxide and splits it into carbon and oxygen; the carbon is absorbed in the sap of the plant as a sugar, and the oxygen is released into the atmosphere. Sunlight is essential, providing the necessary energy. In the tropics, where there is abundant sunlight, plant growth is luxuriant; in far northern and southern latitudes it is sparse. Plants play a most important role in preventing the accumulation of carbon dioxide and in maintaining the supply of oxygen in the air.

Although the air is four-fifths nitrogen, plants have no way of utilizing elemental nitrogen. It is extremely inert and can be put into chemical combination only with great difficulty. The primary rocks contain none, and the nitrogen in soils derived from them must come from other sources. Nature has a most ingenious means of converting the nitrogen of the atmosphere into a soluble form on which plants can feed: certain bacteria in the soil which can absorb elemental nitrogen. Certain plants, called legumes (beans, peas, clover, etc.), grow thriving colonies of the nitrogen-fixing bacteria in nodules on their roots. Cultivation of the legumes builds up the nitrogen content of a soil. The bacteria require food in the form of decaying organic material—manure or turned-under green crops—for their best development, also an alkaline or neutral soil condition.

The soil picks up nitrogen in two additional ways, though the quantities are small: A flash of lightning burns the nitrogen along its path to nitric acid, which the rain washes down to the soil. The natural decomposition of animal excretions produces ammonia, as those around stables know. Such supplies of an important plant food are haphazard. That they work in a fashion is proved by the existence of plant life for millions of years. But man presents a new problem; by crowding into communities he requires the maximum of production from the contiguous food-producing areas. The more that can be grown on an acre, the less labor is required for cultivation and harvesting. Once the food requirements of the plant are known, these can be met with intensive feeding; and, granted good soil and seed and favorable weather conditions, it is possible to get five to seven times more wheat, for example, from the same soil.

Plant foods are primarily soluble compounds of potassium, phosphorus, and nitrogen. They are distributed over the soil, the rains wash them in, and they become part of the soil-solution. This is always in motion, upward toward the surface if evaporation is taking place, downward during rainy periods. Bacterial action converts the salts into complex compounds which, as they come into contact with the hairlike rootlets of the plant, are absorbed and pass into its sap stream. They are carried to all parts of the plant, different organs taking their specific requirements to build cells. It is the reproduction and growth of the cells, of course, which accounts for the plant's growth. Meanwhile, the green foliage has been contributing to the sap stream the organic carbon compounds which it has prepared from the carbon dioxide in the air.

In this country, plant foods are usually prepared in the form of a mixed fertilizer—made in factories equipped not merely to mix purchased compounds but, in many cases, to do a limited amount of processing. Potash is mined as a crude ore, and is purified for agricultural use. For example, in New Mexico there are large deposits of potassium chloride mixed with sodium chloride, about a thousand feet below the surface in a flat seam. The ore is mined much the same as bituminous coal—cut by machine, broken down with explosives, and hoisted to the surface. There it is crushed to coarse grain, and by a mechanical process and the use of special chemical reagents the potassium chloride grains are floated away from the sodium chloride grains. The muriate (potassium chloride) is then dried and shipped to the fertilizer mixer.

In the South and West of the United States, in Tennessee, Florida, and Montana, are large deposits of phosphate rock. Florida produces two varieties: one the gravel called Florida pebble phosphate, the other in large lumps called hard rock phosphate. Tennessee also mines two varieties: brown Tennessee rock, a coarse broken or gravelly form; and blue Tennessee rock, a hard stratified form, mined underground. The Montana rock is hard and stratified in thick seams. Phosphate occurs in all these forms as a mineral, containing a compound of calcium phosphate and calcium fluoride or calcium chloride. The commercial product is graded according to its content of tricalcium phosphate, $Ca_3P_2O_8$.

In the trade this is more commonly called bone phosphate of lime, abbreviated to B.P.L. The commercial grades carry from 60 to 76 per cent of tricalcium phosphate. The Florida pebble is an altered residue of skeletons of land and marine life, for tusks of land animals and teeth of sharks, both altered to the phosphate, yet without change in form or appearance, are found in great quantity in the deposits. The Tennessee and Montana deposits are also of animal origin, but have undergone chemical decomposition and redeposition in transformation to their present form.

As mined, phosphate rock is not soluble in water, and would become useful to plants only after weathering, or soil decomposition. Modern methods of agriculture cannot await this slow natural process. The chemist grinds the rock to powder and treats it with sulphuric acid, which, because it is a much stronger acid than phosphoric, takes some of the calcium away from the tricalcium phosphate, producing a monocalcium phosphate, $CaH_4P_2O_8$, and calcium sulphate. The monocalcium phosphate is soluble in water and therefore immediately available for absorption by the rootlets. This processed material is called *acid phosphate,* and contains from 16 to 20 per cent phosphoric anhydride, P_2O_5. Trade practice in the fertilizer industry has long used the term "phosphoric acid" to designate the anhydride. The acid phosphate is a gray to tan-colored granular material ready for incorporating into the ordinary fertilizer. If phosphoric acid is substituted for sulphuric acid in the process of disintegrating the phosphate rock, a soluble phosphate of much greater concentration is obtained.

Many seeds contain oil, and these vegetable oils play a very important part in our national economy. They are expressed from the seeds by heavy pressure, often facilitated by precooking. The meal that remains in the press may be used as cattle feed, and if unsuited to that purpose, in fertilizer, for it contains nitrogen. So also do the waste products of slaughterhouses, which are cooked and dried and find their way either into cattle, hog, or chicken feed or, if of low grade, into fertilizer. These dried waste products of the meat-packing industry are called *tankage.* In the fertilizer industry, the meals and tankages are called *organics* because the nitrogen in them is in a complex organic combination, as vegetable or animal proteins. Because the organics are by-products of other industries the supply is rather limited. At one time they were an important raw material of the fertilizer industry, but now all the better grades go into feeds.

Coal, being of vegetable origin, also contains nitrogen. When it is converted into coke, some of its nitrogen is liberated in the form of ammonia, and leaves the coke-oven in the gas stream. This is recovered as a water solution when the gas is cooled, or preferably, by scrubbing with sulphuric acid, as sulphate of ammonia, $(NH_4)_2SO_4$, a white crystalline salt whose principal use is in the fertilizer industry.

In the dry desert area of northern Chile there is a large natural deposit of nitrate of soda (Chile nitrate), $NaNO_3$. It has been mined for more than a century. The crude ore is sent to a refining plant where the very soluble nitrate is dissolved out of the insoluble matrix, and the solution evaporated until the nitrate separates as crystal. This is dried and sent to the fertilizer plants, though a great deal is used for direct application to the soil (top-dressing). The nitrate contains about 16 per cent nitrogen. At one time the Chilean nitrate fields were the only source of agricultural nitrogen, but they lost some of their importance to the several by-product nitrogenous materials which could be used in the fertilizer mixtures. In more recent times synthetic processes have been developed for making both ammonia and nitrate, and the natural deposits are meeting most serious competition.

In the feeding of plants the three forms of nitrogen—nitrate, ammonical and organic—are not exactly equivalent. The plant absorbs nitrate nitrogen from the soil solution, and soil to which this form is applied gives quick response, no conversion being necessary. The plant can make only slight use of ammonia; bacteria can transform it to nitrate, but this requires some time. Bacteria also must transform the organic nitrogen to nitrate form before the plant can utilize it; this takes still more time. The better fertilizers use all three forms of nitrogen, affording a long feeding period, practically over the full crop cycle.

About forty years ago a famous English scientist, Sir William Crookes, analyzed the future food supply problem of the world, with particular emphasis upon wheat, the principal food of the white race. His analysis emphasized the fact that there was very little new land adaptable to the cultivation of wheat, and that a growing white population would be in danger of food shortage unless means of increasing the yield per acre could be found.

Nitrogen plays a very important part in wheat growing. With favorable growing conditions, a pound of nitrogen may be expected to increase production by as much as ten to twenty pounds of grain. Sir William estimated that the available supply of Chilean nitrate would be much curtailed, if not exhausted, within twenty-five or thirty years, i.e., around 1930. His report created a tremendous stir throughout the civilized world.

Crookes's original lecture contained the constructive suggestion that the atmosphere, four-fifths of which is nitrogen, constituted an inexhaustible supply, since it is continuously replenished through the death and decay of living matter. But, as stated above, atmospheric nitrogen is not readily assimilable by plants. How could it be made so? Chemists became seriously interested, and within a relatively short time two processes of conversion were developed on a commercial scale. A third process followed a few years later. Today, the world is in no danger of starvation for lack of nitrogen, and conversion from the atmosphere has been in such quantity that prices have dropped by half since 1914. The mining of nitrate in Chile almost ceased, but subsequent improvements in the process of ore treatment have permitted the mining of low-grade ore that was not even included in the original surveys of the nitrate fields.

The first commercial process of converting the inert nitrogen of the air used the idea of the flash of lightning from cloud to earth, which creates a very high temperature along its path through the atmosphere and causes the nitrogen to unite with oxygen to form nitric acid. The chemist and the electrical engineer together set out to reproduce this effect, building an electric furnace in which a very powerful electric arc could be created. Air was then forced through this arc, and at the high temperature prevailing, nitric oxide, NO, was formed. The gases were cooled and scrubbed with water to form a dilute solution of nitric acid. Limestone was dumped into the solution to make calcium nitrate, $Ca(NO_3)_2$, and the solution was evaporated, the salt dried and sent to the fertilizer market. This process requires very large quantities of electric energy and is commercially feasible only where electric power is extremely cheap. It is now practically obsolete.

The second commercial process was described briefly in the preceding chapter in the discussion of the utilization of calcium carbide. The nitrogen in Cyanamid is not directly utilizable by plants; but a few days' exposure of the material in damp soil brings about a chemical transformation to urea:

$$CaCN_2 + 3\,H_2O = (NH_2)_2CO + Ca(OH)_2$$

Urea in turn is converted to nitrate by soil bacteria. The alkaline character of Cyanamid abets the neutralizing of soil acids and promotes the development of soil bacteria. Some two and a half million tons are used per year in the more important agricultural regions of the world. Its manufacture requires only about one-sixth as much electric power as the arc process mentioned above.

The third method, which came into operation during the last war (nitrogen is also a very important ingredient of explosives), starts with a mixture of three volumes of hydrogen and one volume of nitrogen. If the mixture is compressed and passed over a suitable catalyst, the gases combine to form ammonia. The hydrogen is usually obtained by the reaction of steam on hot coke to produce a gas half hydrogen and half carbon monoxide. Steam is added to this gas in large quantity, and the mixture is passed through a conversion apparatus containing a catalyst, oxide of iron with admixture of a little chromium oxide. The steam reacts with the carbon monoxide to form hydrogen and carbon dioxide. This gas mixture is cooled to condense the excess of steam, and then compressed to several hundred pounds per square inch and scrubbed with water. The water dissolves the carbon dioxide (soda water), and the hydrogen and nitrogen are then further compressed to the operating pressure, which varies from 1,500 to 15,000 pounds per square inch according to which of half a dozen processes is chosen. At this high pressure the gas mixture is again scrubbed with a copper solution to remove any other impurities which might interfere with the final conversion.

There are several ways of getting the nitrogen into this mixture. One way is to liquefy air, distill the nitrogen off the liquid, and add it to the hydrogen from the iron converter. Another is to add air to the steam in the first gas generation, the oxygen uniting with the coke to form carbon monoxide, leaving the nitrogen in the gas from the gas machine.

The compressed mixture of highly purified hydrogen and nitrogen is then piped to a heavy-walled steel conversion vessel. Here it passes through a catalyst at red heat—a granular mass of iron containing small amounts of aluminum and potassium. The hydrogen and nitrogen combine to form ammonia. Only a portion of the gas combines in a single pass; and so the gas from the converter is cooled to liquefy the ammonia it contains, and the uncombined and uncondensed gases are returned with fresh hydrogen-nitrogen mixture to the converter. The chemical reactions involved are:

(1) Water gas production
$$C + H_2O = CO + H_2$$

(2) Carbon monoxide conversion
$$CO + H_2 + H_2O = CO_2 + 2 H_2$$

(3) Ammonia conversion
$$N_2 + 3 H_2 = 2 NH_3$$

The ammonia may be absorbed in sulphuric acid to form ammonium sulphate, or in nitric acid to form ammonium nitrate. Nitric acid may be made by oxidizing the ammonia, and neutralized with limestone to produce calcium nitrate, or with soda ash to form sodium nitrate. All these salts may find use in the fertilizer industry. Thus the three processes for converting the atmosphere's inexhaustible supply of nitrogen make impossible the starvation of Sir William Crookes's foreboding.

An exhaustive study of the feeding of plants indicates that other elements than nitrogen, phosphorus, and potassium are necessary for the highest crop returns. The quantities required are small, and most soils contain sufficient quantity. Magnesium is one of these: a deficiency can be supplied by ground dolomite, a carbonate of calcium and magnesium, $CaMg(CO_3)_2$. Nature has placed abundant supplies of this rock in many places. Manganese is required by certain plants—tomatoes in Florida, for example, the Florida sandy soils containing almost none. A fraction of 1 per cent of a soluble manganese salt, manganese sulphate, $MnSO_4$, is added to the fertilizers used for this culture. Zinc assists in the growth of pecans in Georgia, and a small amount of zinc sulphate, $ZnSO_4$, is distributed in the pecan orchards. Boron, in the form of sodium borate, $Na_2B_4O_7 \cdot 10\,H_2O$, in small amount has a beneficial effect in certain culture, but in larger amount is quite toxic to the growing plant.

Many millions of tons of these fertilizers and fertilizer materials are consumed each year in this country. They are most carefully compounded to meet the needs of various crops and of the various types of soils. Their sale is under state supervision, and guaranteed analyses and carefully labeled packages are mandatory.

The chemical industry is also called upon for products that affect specific functions of a plant. For example, certain compounds stimulate the growth of roots on a cut stem, and enormously increase a slip's chance of growth. The cuttings are soaked for a definite number of minutes in a dilute water solution of such compound just before planting. This requires care and experience, for overtreatment is fatal. One such compound in wide use is indolbutyric acid—an organic compound of the base indol—an intermediate closely related to indigo dye—with butyric acid. The synthesis is very complex, requiring a long series of chemical manipulations, and the cost is relatively high. Fortunately very small quantities are needed.

The apple grower has always suffered great loss through the "summer drop." A remedy is found in alpha naphthalene acetic acid, which is applied in dilute water solution as a summer spray. The chemical formula $C_{10}H_7CH_2COOH$ seems relatively simple, yet for production four raw materials and five steps in processing are required.

In addition to these contributions to the feeding and propagation of plants, the chemist provides the insecticides and fungicides which save our crops from pests. There are three classes of pests: the fungi, the sucking insects, the chewing insects.

The fungi are low forms of vegetable life propagated by spores, which frequently infest the seeds. The spores can be devitalized by soaking the seeds in a dilute water solution of formaldehyde and subsequently drying them. This is a troublesome procedure. Dry dusts that can be tumbled with the seed are preferred. The essential active ingredients of such dusts are mercury, copper, cadmium, and nickel in the form of oxides, hydrates, or carbonates. The organic-metal salts are also used, a combination of phenol and mercury being particularly effective as a seed disinfectant. For the control of fungi on the growing plants, a spray containing copper hydroxide (Bordeaux mixture) or nickel hydroxide is used. Sulphur dust is quite effective for destroying the common mildew.

The sucking insects feed by inserting a proboscis through the bark and sucking the sap which should nourish the plant. They must be attacked with poisons that destroy on contact with their body, or that interfere with their breathing. The common household fly sprays destroy by contact. They contain pyrethrum dissolved in a volatile petroleum oil. Pyrethrum is extracted from a flower of that name, and little chemistry is involved in its preparation. Rotenone, extracted from the derris root, is also used for this purpose. But the most important contact poison is nicotine. It is extracted from tobacco stems, scrap, and waste with a solution of alkali. The solution is then concentrated and neutralized with sulphuric acid, forming nicotine sulphate. While these poisons are generally used as a spray, they may also be mixed with an inert powder, such as ground talc, to form a dusting compound. Oil sprays, made by emulsifying petroleum oils in water in the presence of soap to hold the emulsion, are effective against sucking insects, as they clog the breathing organs.

Contact insecticides are effective against soft-bodied lice and worms, but much less so against armored insects, such as beetles. Sprays or dusts are not effective against scale insects (usually soft-bodied but covered by a hard impenetrable shield or scale), of which there are many varieties that play havoc with citrus culture in California. They are best controlled by a toxic gas. A canvas tent is thrown over a tree and filled with hydrocyanic acid, an exceedingly poisonous gas lighter than air which diffuses throughout the enclosed space. The scale insects breathe it and die. Sodium cyanide or calcium cyanide (each a product of the electrochemical industry, extensively used in extracting gold and silver from ores) is heated with sulphuric acid to produce hydrocyanic acid. It has a very low boiling point and leaves the generator as vapor, which is condensed to liquid by cooling with refrigerated brine. The fumigation must be done at night when the leaves are inactive (not absorbing carbon dioxide), in order not to injure the foliage.

Scale insects on deciduous trees that are dormant in the winter can be killed by spraying with lime-sulphur solutions. These sprays are made by boiling milk of lime and sulphur together—a hazardous operation requiring great care and skill.

The chewing insects are usually controlled by the arsenate poisons—arsenates of lead, copper, and calcium. Many metallic ores, particularly those of copper, contain arsenic. The first step in the production of the metal is oxidizing or roasting. This converts arsenic to arsenious oxide, As_2O_3, often called white arsenic, which is quite volatile and travels with the gases from the roaster to a separator for recovery. White arsenic can easily be converted to arsenious acid, H_3AsO_3, and to the corresponding salts—for example, sodium arsenite, Na_3AsO_3. The sodium salt is soluble in water, and will kill any plant on which it is sprayed. It cannot, therefore, be used as an insecticide, but is excellent for killing weeds where cattle are never likely to feed. The arsenious acid, H_3AsO_3, in water solution is readily converted to arsenic acid, H_3AsO_4, by treatment with strong oxidizing agents like chlorine and nitric acid. Arsenic acid reacts with calcium hydroxide, milk of lime, to form an insoluble calcium arsenate, $Ca_3(AsO_4)_2$. Lead arsenate may be formed in like manner by using a soluble lead salt, usually lead acetate. Arsenates to be used as insecticides must be most carefully prepared, and must contain no water-soluble arsenic compounds, which seriously damage growing plants. They are supplied dry for dusting, or suspended in water, for spraying. Soap, casein, or a similar adhesive material is added both to the dust form and to the spray to make them adhere to foliage.

Arsenic is so poisonous and persistent that indiscriminate use is very dangerous, and health authorities have set standards of maximum permissible arsenic content on fruits. To comply with these regulations, sprayed fruit must be washed with weak acids or other special detergents to remove the spray residues. Such washing introduces a problem of damage to the keeping quality. Recently cryolite, a fluoride of aluminum and sodium, Na_3AlF_6, has been tried as a substitute for the arsenicals; but its consumption is still very small compared to the tons of arsenic compounds used each year. Its great advantage is that it washes off very easily.

Food products are subject to insect infestation during storage. The problem of control in such circumstances is entirely different. The foodstuff may be in large bins, in packages, in slack casks or crates. Grain, flour, dried fruits, breakfast foods, tobacco—all must be protected from weevils, worms, and the like. But there must be no residue of insecticide in the food product, nor can the flavor be altered in any degree. Gaseous fumigants or very volatile liquids are used for this purpose. Carbon disulphide, CS_2, and hydrocyanic acid, HCN, are the two most widely used fumigants. Several organic compounds like chloropicrin, CCl_3NO_2, have special application. Many agricultural imports are quarantined at our borders and fumigated to prevent the entrance of new insect pests into the country.

The larger food companies use many chemical controls in grading their products, checking their purity, improving their methods and packaging. Wheat is graded roughly by the weight per bushel, the heavier varieties being more valuable for breadmaking; the lighter are diverted to the cake, pastry, and self-raising flours. The heavier wheats contain most nitrogen, and the final grading and blending by the large millers is based on this nitrogen content—a laboratory control problem. The demand for extremely white flours necessitates the use of bleaching agents, the commonest being a peroxide of nitrogen, N_2O_4. Better knowledge of the food values in the darker-colored flours is lessening the emphasis on whiteness.

The self-raising flours are factory mixtures of flour and the ingredients of baking powder. The chemistry of these compounds is relatively simple, but their functioning is complicated. A harmless gas must be generated in the dough or batter, in an amount that will not escape, at precisely the stage in the baking at which the mass has lost fluidity and is about to set to the final consistency. For the desirable texture the bubbles must be small and evenly distributed.

This intricate problem has been solved by a mixture of two compounds which are inert to each other in the dry state but react in the presence of moisture at a certain temperature—one of the products being a harmless gas, the other a harmless residue. The gas produced by all such agents is carbon dioxide, quite innocuous in the quantity involved. Its source is baking soda (sodium bicarbonate, $NaHCO_3$), a very weak compound which any stronger acid will decompose, liberating carbon dioxide and forming the sodium salt of the chosen acid. Most of the more common acids are liquids and cannot be used because they would react immediately on mixing; therefore an acid salt, such as potassium bitartrate, $KHC_4H_4O_6$ (cream of tartar), or monocalcium phosphate, $CaH_4P_2O_8$, is used instead. Sodium aluminum sulphate may also be used as the acid ingredient, for it acts as an acid when moistened. These are stable, dry solid materials, and may be considered as half neutralized acids, yet still possessing enough acid character to react with alkaline materials. Baking powder is a dry, prepared mixture of the bicarbonate and the acid salt. When mixed with flour, moistened, and heated in the oven it gives off minute bubbles of carbon dioxide which fluff up the cake just as the heat is setting the mass.

The porosity and lightness of bread result from a very different chemical process employing yeast. This is a plant of the fungus type, grown in solution, and must be fed like any other plant. The base of its food is starch and sugar, or malted grain. From the chemical industry come nitrogenous and phosphatic materials, similar to but purer than those used in the fertilizer industry. Yeast is grown in the dark and cannot feed itself from the air. The yeast plant contains an enzyme (an organic catalyst) that can convert sugar into alcohol and carbon dioxide. When yeast is added to dough, the carbon dioxide evolved causes the "raising." The alcohol, in small amount, evaporates during baking.

$$C_6H_{12}O_6 = 2\ CO_2 + 2\ C_2H_5OH$$

The baking powder, self-raising flour, and yeast industries require more than a hundred thousand tons of chemicals a year.

The packing houses are not large consumers of chemicals so far as food products are concerned, but the reverse is true of their by-product adjuncts. They use common salt and saltpeter (potassium nitrate, KNO_3) as preservatives and herbs for flavoring. Sausage casings are sometimes synthetic cellulose products.

There are two newly developed processes of "tenderizing" meat. One uses ultraviolet light (that is light of lesser wave length than the visible violet) which, by a photochemical reaction not thoroughly understood, seems to break down the tough connective tissue in the flesh. The other method achieves the same result through chemical action, brought about by an enzyme from unripe papaya.

The canning and preserving industries have called upon the chemist for pectin, the compound which causes fruit juices to jell. It is extracted from fruit refuse once thrown away. A better knowledge of fruit preservation has diminished the use of chemical preservatives, such as formaldehyde, benzoate of soda, salicylic acid. In the very small amount ordinarily required to assure preservation, they are quite harmless; but their presence must be indicated on the label, and the customer suspects the use of poor raw material and careless processing.

All food handling industries require large amounts of soaps, cleaning compounds, and disinfectants, to keep their apparatus sterile and their plants clean.

The chemist has rendered outstanding service to the food producing and conserving industries. He has evolved a rational understanding of the feeding of crops, and has made in great quantity

MODERN CONTACT SULPHURIC ACID PLANT

The catalytic mass is in the insulated tower to the left; a cooler on the
right

NITRIC ACID PLANT
Absorbing units in towers right and left

the chemical compounds required by an intensive agriculture. He has given means of control of the vast insect hordes that interfere so much with the production of food. The new knowledge of synthetic chemistry is now creating new materials and methods of pest control. The day of food shortage is being postponed to an ever more distant future, thanks to the chemist and his laboratory.

Chapter VII

SHELTER

After food, shelter is man's greatest need. Our ancestors used caves; their descendants who wandered to the tropics still get along quite happily with a few sticks covered with thatch. The ancient Egyptians made bricks from clay, and even knew how to plasticize the poorer sorts (Chapter II).

Mortar made from burned and slacked lime is found in very ancient structures. But lime-mortar is weak, and sets slowly, for its hardening is largely due to the absorption of carbon dioxide from the air (forming calcium carbonate). It has little resistance to water, as we unfortunately discover when the plumbing leaks and our plastered ceilings weaken and fall.

Long ago the Romans developed a superior cement with hydraulic properties. Its setting was due to a recrystallization resulting from the addition of water. They found that if certain types of impure limestone, carrying a goodly portion of clay, were burned at a high temperature and then ground fine, they would set very hard when mixed with water. The clay, a silicate of alumina, combined to some extent with the lime at the high temperature of the kiln, to form a calcium aluminum silicate. This is of not very definite composition, being a mixture of several chemical compounds. When it is wetted, a recrystallization takes place, the hardening or setting being due to the rearrangement and interlacing of the crystals as the water enters into combination with the silicates. The Romans used these cements in their magnificent aqueducts and bridges.

Modern Portland cement is an improvement on this Roman product. It is not a definite chemical compound, but a mixture of tricalcium aluminate, $3\,CaO\cdot Al_2O_3$; tricalcium silicate,

3 CaO·SiO$_2$; dicalcium silicate, 2 CaO·SiO$_2$; and a small amount of free lime, CaO. It may be made from a wide variety of raw materials, the prerequisite being that the residue after heating to a temperature of approximately 2500° Fahrenheit shall be a sintered product of about this composition:

Lime (CaO)	62–65 per cent
Silica (SiO$_2$)	22–24
Alumina (Al$_2$O$_3$)	6– 8
Ferric oxide (Fe$_2$O$_3$)	2– 4
Magnesia (MgO)	1– 3

In eastern Pennsylvania, lying geologically between the slates and the true limestones, there was a natural cement rock whose constituent limestone and slate were mixed in just the correct proportions to come within the above specifications. For a Portland cement, all that was necessary was to quarry this, grind, burn, and grind it again. But the quantity of such natural raw material was limited, and the deposit is now exhausted.

However, it is quite possible to attain the composition above by several mixtures of readily available materials; for example, limestone and clay; limestone and shale; oystershell in place of the limestone; marl and clay; blast-furnace slag and limestone. In other words, the materials for Portland cement are widely distributed. Even in the processing these combinations differ only in small details. The raw materials are ground fine, either in prepared mixture or separately—usually in wet mills. The thick slurry is run into large storage tanks, thoroughly mixed, and a final adjustment made to exact composition. It is then pumped to the kilns, where it is dried and burned at a temperature that just melts it, so that it sticks together in small nodules—the so-called cement clinker. The clinker is stored in the open to age, for water does not affect it. The last step in the process is to grind the clinker in a dry mill to fine powder.

Cement made from the ground clinker alone would set in a few minutes, too fast to permit proper placing in the forms, many of which are intricate. Therefore gypsum or calcium sulphate is added to the clinker in the cement milling operation to slow up the setting time. The amount varies with the use to which the cement is put; for average purposes it is about 2 per cent. This increases the setting time to about two hours, during which it may be transported to the form, placed, and tamped before becoming too stiff —all without affecting the final strength.

The mills used for grinding the raw materials are tube mills: long cylindrical steel shells lined with hard steel plates, and filled with steel balls. They rotate on a horizontal axis, the tumbling and rolling of the heavy balls pulverizing the feed. The operation is continuous, with the raw materials and water fed through a trunnion on one end, and the thick slurry passing out through a trunnion at the discharge end. The clinker is ground in a similar mill, except that the charge is dry.

The raw materials are burned in rotary kilns—long cylindrical tubes, the larger units some twelve feet in diameter and four hundred feet long. They are fitted with a series of tires, resting on rollers, so that in operation they can be slowly rotated. The kiln slopes from the upper feed end to the lower discharge end, and the rotation advances the charge slowly down the kiln. The lower two-thirds is lined with blocks of firebrick, to withstand the high temperature in the hottest zone, about 2500° Fahrenheit. The wet mix enters the upper end of the kiln. As it comes in contact with the hot gases from the fire, water is driven off. The dry powder moves slowly down the kiln, heating to the temperature of 1500°, when the calcium carbonate from the limestone is decomposed into lime and carbon dioxide. At the hottest point the lime combines with the silica and the alumina in the charge, and fuses just enough to stick together into clinker. Kilns are fired by natural gas, fuel oil, or, more commonly, pulverized bituminous coal blown in by a blast of air.

When moistened with water and left to age, Portland cement sets or hardens. The several compounds, silicates and aluminates, are decomposed by the water and take up some of it, forming hydrates which crystallize, the crystals matting and growing through each other; any excess water dries out, and the cement is set. Portland cement will set under water. The setting process begins an hour or two after mixing with water, controlled in this case by the admixture of the gypsum during manufacture; but for the first twenty-four hours the set mass has little strength, and must not be disturbed. After several days the forms may be removed, and it will bear light loads. In a week it acquires considerable strength, and this continues to increase for months.

Cement is used alone only for the finishing of surfaces; for mortar, it is mixed with clean sharp sand, one part of cement to two or three parts of sand. The principal application is in the form of *concrete,* a mixture of cement, sand, and crushed stone. This should be so proportioned that all voids between the individual constituents are filled completely. A good concrete contains one part cement, two parts sand, four parts crushed stone. A month after placing, this will show a compressive strength of about 2,500 pounds per square inch. Cement is never used in tension, such stress being taken care of by steel reinforcing embedded in the concrete.

For emergency work, particularly repairs, a material that sets to a strong mass in the quickest possible time is desired; yet the initial set must be delayed long enough to permit proper placement. Some improvement in this respect over the ordinary Portland cement may be attained by modification of the burning, and by finer grinding. A wholly different type of cement, which gets as strong in twenty-four hours as Portland cement does in a month, is made by fusing bauxite, the common ore of aluminum, with limestone, either in an electric furnace or in a shaft furnace, and grinding the fused mass very fine. It is naturally slow in its initial set and requires no gypsum.

In the past, building materials were not chosen for their capacity to prevent the leakage of heat; but it has become general practice to supplement the usual materials with heat insulators— substances that resist the flow of heat, outward in the winter, inward in the summer. Light porous materials make the best heat insulators. They may be of animal origin, like coarse wool; or vegetable, like cork, various fibers, dispersed wood; or mineral, like asbestos, mica, glass, or rock wool.

Animal fibers are subject to moth attack, and the chemist must mothproof them with alkaline fluorides. Some vegetable fibers contain enough sugar to attract rodents, which can be frustrated by impregnating them with arsenic compounds. Rock wool is nothing but a glassy slag (silica, alumina, and lime fused together) blown into fine threads.

Many of these insulating products attract moisture, or soak up water that happens to come into contact with them; sometimes rapid temperature changes cause them to sweat. When wet they not only lose their insulating value, but sag and become displaced. The chemist waterproofs them with an odorless, heavy mineral oil containing a dispersing agent, or with a rosin compound.

The shingle and slate are slowly giving way to newer fabricated materials. Prepared roofing is a textile base impregnated with asphaltum, a complex hydrocarbon found in various parts of the world, and also a residue from the refining of certain types of petroleum. Prepared tars are also used; multiple layers of heavy paper or fabric impregnated with tar are laid down and sealed together with hot tar (coal-tar pitch). This type of roofing can be used on a horizontal or only slightly sloping roof. However, asphalt and tar compounds are affected by sunlight, and become brittle. The surface is therefore covered with an inert mineral, such as slate chips, granulated slag, or tile.

Ceramic and glass products are important building materials. Brick and tile seem as old as history. They are made from a plastic clay, which is worked into a doughlike mass, molded to form, dried in the air, and burned in a kiln at a temperature high enough to just fuse or sinter the particles so that they bond together. The essential ingredient of clay is a hydrous aluminum silicate, kaolinite, $H_4Al_2Si_2O_9$, from which the hydrogen is driven by a low red heat, leaving the anhydrous silicate $Al_2Si_2O_7$. In the pure form this can be sintered only at a very high temperature, above 3000° Fahrenheit. Small amounts of impurities, common in most varieties —such as potassium compounds and oxides of iron, lime, soda— lower the fusion temperature, often greatly. Brick and tile of the ordinary red color contain oxides of iron and burn at a relatively low temperature. The firebrick used for furnace linings is made of a very pure clay and is always light-colored, showing the absence of deleterious impurities. Oxides of manganese are added to the clay mix to make a very dark, even black, brick. Oxide of chromium will give a greenish color to the brick.

Light-colored wall tile and porcelain fixtures are made from a prepared mixture of white kaolinite, ground feldspar ($K_2Al_2Si_6O_{16}$), and ground white quartz (SiO_2). This mix is not unlike that used for the body of ordinary chinaware. The plastic mass is molded to form and slowly dried to a firm structure. It is then washed on one surface with an easily fusible mixture containing lead oxide (PbO), tin oxide (SnO_2), ground feldspar, and ground silica, and fired in a kiln. This fusible wash actually melts in the kiln to form the glazed surface. Suitable oxides may be added to the glaze if colors other than white are desired. Compositions not unlike the glaze are also prepared for coating iron. After firing they adhere strongly. The formulation of the glazes or enamels for coating iron presents a complex chemical problem, for unless the glaze expands and contracts equally with the iron under the shock of alternating hot and cold water it will chip.

Glass, though homogeneous, is a solid solution and not a chemical compound. There are many varieties. At one extreme is the common green or brown bottle glass; at the other, scientifically exact optical glass. Soft glass has a low softening temperature; hard glass, a high one. Glass may be had in all colors of the rainbow, white and black; opaque, translucent, transparent, iridescent. Cut glass for the table has almost the brilliance of the diamond. The dull glass of the cooking utensil takes the shock of the baking oven. Glass is a material of marvelous adaptability.

Window and plate glass are silicates of sodium and lead, but of different composition. The raw materials of these must be selected with extreme care, for foreign metallic oxides will color the product: The silica is a washed sand, or crushed sandstone; the sodium is derived from soda ash, the lead oxide from litharge, PbO. These ingredients are mixed in carefully weighed amounts, and melted down, either in a pot or in a large open-tank furnace, at a temperature of about 2500° Fahrenheit. A typical window glass contains 72 per cent silica, 12 per cent lead oxide, and 13 per cent sodium oxide. Sometimes a little nitrate of soda is added to counteract color coming from impurities in the raw materials. A very small amount of manganese dioxide, MnO_2, is often used to further neutralize slight yellow tinge.

The finest crystal glass, so much admired because of its great brilliance, contains 55 per cent silica, 33 per cent lead oxide, and 12 per cent potassium oxide, K_2O. The raw materials for its production are particularly free of foreign coloring oxides.

The Pyrex glass of cooking utensils contains approximately 80 per cent silica, 2 per cent alumina, Al_2O_3, 4 per cent sodium oxide, 12 per cent boric oxide, B_2O_3, and 2 per cent miscellaneous oxides. Like most solid materials glass expands when warmed, and has very poor heat conductivity. This combination of properties causes glass to crack when subjected to sudden changes of temperature, for differential stresses are set up throughout the mass. Pure silica has almost no temperature expansion, and a red-hot piece may be dropped into ice-water without cracking. Pyrex glass contains a large proportion of silica to take the maximum advantage of this property. Recently a new type of glass has been put on the market —made in the usual manner and pressed or blown to form. The components, other than silica, are dissolved out by acid, leaving a porous skeleton of the silica. This is heated to a very high temperature which shrinks and frits it to a solid, almost as resistant to temperature changes as pure silica. This can be formed into intricate shapes much more easily than pure silica.

The crown type of glass, so important to the lens manufacturer and photographer, is a soda glass to which a little lime has been added. The green and brown bottle glasses owe their color to oxides of iron from impure raw materials. Colored glasses are made by adding various metallic oxides to the glass batch: cobalt oxide for dark blue; copper oxide for greenish blue; selenium oxide for red; manganese oxide for purple; uranium oxide for light yellow. Phosphates and fluorides are added to make translucent or milk glass.

Safety glass, originally developed for protective goggles and shields, now universally used in automobiles, railway carriages, and for transparent protective shields, is a single- or double-deck sandwich with a sheet of plastic material between each two layers of glass. The first plastic used was celluloid (Chapter XIII), which yellows and loses transparency on exposure to sunlight. Cellulose acetate replaced celluloid with greater satisfaction. Today polyvinyl butyral has the field. (Plastics themselves are unlikely to replace glass for automobile windshields for they are relatively soft and scratch easily. Road dust acts as an abrasive and makes the surface of plastics rough and opaque. For airplanes they are very satisfactory, for this conveyance operates in a relatively dust-free atmosphere.)

The great disadvantage of glass has been its brittleness and its tendency to shatter into sharp, jagged fragments. But "tempering" now gives glass of great strength and elasticity. It will break under great stress, but into small rounded beads instead of the old vicious slivers.

Wood is still an important structural material in this country. Under favorable conditions and with reasonable care it has an unusually long life. Wooden houses have been standing for several centuries. Wood is attacked by fungi, insects, and worms. Impregnation with creosote oil from coal tar makes wood proof against the marine borer, termites, and fungi. While simple dipping is partially satisfactory, the best method of impregnating wood with creosote oil is to put the timber in great metal cylinders and force the oil into the wood under pressure. Large timbers can be saturated to the very center. The odor of creosote persists, and creosoted lumber is rarely used in house construction. Wood for that purpose is impregnated with a soluble arsenic compound. Zinc chloride solutions are often used for protection against fungi, especially in mine timbers.

Plywood has become an important construction material in recent years. It is made as follows: a log of water-soaked wood is revolved against a sharp and accurately set knife which shaves off a broad and continuous sheet that may be as thin as one-eighth inch.

Three, five, or more sheets (an odd number) are piled together, with adhesive between sheets. The direction of the grain is reversed in the alternate sheets. The piles are placed in a heavy hydraulic press, with heated spacers, or platens, at the top and bottom of each unit, and the whole dried under pressure.

The first adhesive used in ordinary plywood was glue; but this absorbs moisture and softens, and is not satisfactory for outdoor use. Casein glue, though less sensitive to moisture, is little better. Plastics of the phenolic or amino types (Chapter XIII) form a truly waterproof bond between the plies, and make them stronger and stiffer than steel, weight for weight. This bonding of plywood is the outcome of long and complex research, and makes it usable in airplane construction, prefabricated housing, and outdoor sheathing. Plywood seems to have a big future.

The great need of the construction industry is a new material than can be fabricated by mass production methods. Bricks may still be used, but they must be laid by hand, one at a time, as they were thousands of years ago. Concrete is unsatisfactory for homes because of the great expense of suitable forms. Many of the prefabricated materials talked about do not have the durability the public expects. Something new is needed, and it will probably be a chemist who will discover it.

CHAPTER VIII

CLOTHING

The native in the African bush does not need the textile chemist for the slim strip of hide that suffices for his wardrobe. Nor do the Laplanders who clothe themselves in the skin of the seal or the reindeer. But in America the transformation of raw materials into finished garments is a billion-dollar industry.

Animals supply, in addition to leather, three raw materials: wool, silk, and casein (from which a new synthetic yarn has been produced in the past few years). From the vegetable kingdom come cotton and linen and a large number of plant fibers of limited utility. But men have not been satisfied with what nature provides. Today, in addition to these natural products we have three classes of synthetic yarns: the viscose type of rayon, the cellulose acetate type, and the amino type (represented by Nylon).

Chemically, wool is a complex albuminoid, rich in amino acids and, oddly enough, containing a small percentage of sulphur. Structurally, it consists of scales arranged in three concentric layers. The outer layer is hard and hornlike, with flat, overlapping scales; and it is this scaly structure that causes the individual filaments to lock together when spun, giving great strength to the yarn. The general treatment of wool for spinning was described in Chapter I.

Silk is somewhat similar to wool in its chemical composition, but does not contain sulphur. The silkworm or caterpillar converts the vegetable protein of its food into a liquid which it expresses through a double spinneret. The two continuous filaments are cemented together by a gluelike substance called sericin. The double strand hardens on exposure to the air, and thus preserves its individuality in the cocoon, which may contain from one to three thousand feet of filament.

The cocoons are sorted by skilled graders, and those of like quality are thrown into a pan of hot water in order to kill the caterpillar inside, and soften the sericin. The filaments from several cocoons are brought together, thrown onto a revolving reel, and unwound from the cocoons. A very slight twist is given during this reeling. The sericin hardens again as it cools, binding the filaments into a somewhat stiff wiry thread. This is the raw silk of commerce. Its pale yellow color is due to the sericin coating, the true filament being a creamy white. The waste produced in this reeling operation, as well as the fiber from damaged cocoons, is saved and ultimately finds its way into *spun* silk thread and yarn, used for the heavier textiles. A single filament averages five ten-thousandths of an inch in diameter.

The first operation on the raw silk is called *throwing*. Depending on the size of the final thread to be made up, enough skeins (each having some five double filaments) are thrown into a soap-oil bath, to soften but not dissolve the sericin. The strands are brought together, given a slight twist, and reeled again. The hardening sericin binds this new thread together, which contains about 80 per cent fiber and 20 per cent sericin. Depending upon what fabric the thread will be used for, more or less of this sericin is removed by hot neutral soap solutions. The more of sericin is removed, the softer the yarn and the more readily it can be bleached and dyed. The dyes used are those suited to animal fibers; bleaching is done by hydrogen peroxide, H_2O_2, always in neutral solutions, for silk is dissolved by alkali.

Casein is a protein compound containing a small amount of phosphorus. About 3.5 per cent of cow's milk is casein. It is separated after removal of the cream or butterfat, by treating skimmed fresh milk with hydrochloric acid until it is decidedly acid. A curd then separates out and is skimmed off, washed with water, and dissolved in dilute caustic soda solution. This is again precipitated by hydrochloric acid, and washed. The process may be repeated several times before a pure product is obtained. This is dried at a low temperature. The casein molecule is a highly polymerized one, and its molecular weight is above 100,000.

Its property of dissolving in a weak alkali solution, and of precipitating again when the solution has been acidulated, is utilized in the preparation of "synthetic wool." A solution so prepared is expressed through a spinneret submerged below the surface of an acid bath. The emerging filaments are "set" by the acid and are picked up in a rotating basket. They are then cut into short lengths, carded, and spun. The filaments of this fiber are smooth, and in consequence the yarn is weaker than yarn made of natural wool; fabrics made from synthetic wool are not as warm. It is chiefly used in very heavy fabrics, such as overcoatings, and is often mixed with wool to increase the wearing qualities.

About 60 per cent of the clothing of the world is made from cotton. Its filament consists of a single cell of cellulose, $(C_6H_{10}O_5)_n$, which tapers to a point at the end opposite the attachment to the seed. While growing, the filament is hollow, and sap flows in this central canal. When ripe, the sap has been absorbed and the cell wall has collapsed, obliterating the canal. The filament is then like a flat, twisted ribbon. This twisted spiral form gives it its spinning qualities, for it makes the fibers stick together into a strong thread. The length of the filament determines the value of the cotton; the lowest grades are about three-quarters inch long, the top grades one and one-half inches. Cotton is nearly pure cellulose. A little wax, some albuminoids, and ash and mineral matter together make less than 2 per cent of its weight.

Cotton requires no chemical preparation before carding and spinning into yarn. Only very little is bleached in yarn form. In the usual unbleached form, cotton yarn is woven into "gray goods." Before these are dyed and finished they are bleached. First the wax on the fiber is removed by boiling in dilute alkali solutions (when sufficiently weak these do not affect cellulose). Bleaching is usually done in hypochlorite (NaClO) solution, which is made by dissolving chlorine gas in a solution of soda ash, or of caustic soda. After bleaching, the cloth is treated with dilute acid to neutralize any remaining alkali, and then thoroughly washed to remove all remaining chemicals. White goods are starched and ironed before marketing, as are colored and printed fabrics.

In the very fine printed cottons, the finishing operations are much more elaborate, though not essentially different in character from those described. In order that sharp multi-colored designs may be transferred to the fabric, the cloth is first singed by running rapidly through a series of intense gas flames to remove any loose fiber or lint. The boiling out of the wax is prolonged, and bleaching and souring are more exact. The cloth, when ready for printing, is nearly pure cellulose. In a modern bleachery, these operations are continuous and highly mechanized, miles of cloth passing in a continuous band through the various baths, dryers and printing machines.

After cotton the most widely used clothing material is linen, which comes from flax, a plant indigenous to many countries in the temperate zone. In America, flax is grown principally for its seed, source of the linseed oil used in the paint industry.

Flax has the important economic advantage of growing in climates too cold for cotton. Its stalks are quite woody when mature. The leaves and seed are removed by machinery, and the denuded stems are bound into bundles and submerged in either running or stagnant water to ferment. This process of *retting* softens the natural gums and washes them out, leaving only the woody fiber, a relatively pure cellulose. Further removal of the gums is accomplished by spreading the straw in thin layers in the air and sunlight. Finally, the fibers are completely separated from any adhering foreign matter by special "breaking" machines. Nevertheless, the cleaned fiber, which is cellular in structure and one to two inches in length, still contains considerable glutinous material and has a silvery to gray color. The individual fibers are about the same diameter as cotton fibers, but differ from the latter, in that the filaments contain knots or joints. These serve to hold the spun yarn together. The bleaching of linen is similar to that of cotton, but because it removes most of the glutinous matter, bleached linen is much weaker than unbleached.

The chemist has long attempted to decompose flax straw by chemical means, for if this operation could be speeded up, linen production might eventually be mechanized and adapted to American conditions. He has not been successful, and linen production is largely from countries where labor is cheap.

Many plants contain fibrous material—jute, sisal, ramie, manila; but these are used for cordage, burlap, mats, and backing for floor coverings. There is little chemistry in their preparation.

Because of its luster, softness, and filminess, natural silk has always been a popular material for textiles; but the hand labor required in its culture and preparation makes it costly, and substitutes that could be produced mechanically were long sought.

The earliest artificial silk to reach commercial application was a pyroxylin. Pyroxylin is a soluble nitrocellulose (see Chapter XIII), which comes from cotton. It was put into solution in a mixture of alcohol and ether and forced through a spinneret. The solute was then separated, or the solvent evaporated, giving a bundle of distinct filaments, which in turn could be spun into a thread or yarn.

But the nitrocellulose yarn was too inflammable for use in cloth, and it was found necessary to denitrate it with sodium sulphohydrate, NaSH. This powerful reducing agent destroys the nitro compound, and causes regeneration of the cellulose, while preserving the filament form. The pyroxylin product with the luster and general appearance of natural silk became known as "artificial silk," but was much less strong and elastic than the product of the silkworm.

This relatively short-lived process was followed by another method of putting cellulose into solution—one that has persisted to this day, giving the largest production of silk substitute. Cellulose in the form of wood pulp (Chapter IX) is soaked for twenty-four hours under most carefully controlled temperature, in a solution of caustic soda of 18 per cent strength. This forms sodium cellulose:

$$C_6H_{10}O_5 + NaOH = C_6H_9O_4 \cdot ONa + H_2O$$

(Since the degree of polymerization of the cellulose molecule is not definitely known, equations of the type above are symbolic, even though they do indicate quantitative relationships.) The excess of caustic soda solution absorbed by the soft pulp is expressed in a powerful hydraulic press. The slightly damp cake from the press is shredded by machine, to a fluffy mass, which is further reacted upon by carbon disulphide, CS_2, in a rotary mixer. This forms cellulose xanthogenate,

$$C_6H_9O_4Na + CS_2 = C_6H_9O_4 \cdot O \cdot NaCS_2$$

which dissolves readily in dilute caustic soda solution, and after most careful filtering to remove every trace of insoluble matter, goes to storage to "age." The chemistry of the aging process is not exactly known, but it is believed that the xanthogenate slowly decomposes and starts to re-form cellulose, becoming very thick and viscous—hence the name *viscose* given to this type of synthetic fiber.

When the aging is completed, the solution is forced through a spinneret submerged in a solution of sulphuric acid, magnesium sulphate, and sodium sulphate. The filaments coagulate at the instant of formation because of precipitation of cellulose, and are given a slight twist as they drop into a revolving basket. After thorough washing to remove all chemical reagents, they are bleached, dried, and wound on a spool or put into a skein, ready for the knitter or weaver. This is a mechanized process from end to end and uses very little labor up to the sorting, packing, and shipping. In fact one version of the process uses a wholly automatic machine to express the filaments, wash, dry, and spool the product. Most exacting chemical control is required in the preparation of the viscose solution.

A somewhat finer and more elastic filament is made by the cuprammonium, or Bemberg, process. Cellulose, preferably a highly purified cotton lint, is dissolved in copper-ammonium hydroxide, $Cu(NH_3)_4(OH)_2$—itself made by dissolving copper hydroxide in aqua ammonia. This forms an intensely blue viscous solution, which is pressed through a many-holed spinneret submerged in weak sulphuric acid. The copper and the ammonia are dissolved away from the cellulose, which sets in the acid bath. By a slight tension on the filament as it forms, it is caused to assume an extremely small diameter, quite as fine as that of the natural-silk filament. The bundle of filaments is twisted into yarn, bleached, dried, and spooled or skeined for market. This yarn is used for knitting very thin stockings and weaving fine cloth.

The three synthetic fibers just described are all reconstructed cellulose. Because silk is an albuminoid, chemically unrelated to cellulose, *artificial silk* has been abandoned as a name in favor of *rayon*. But the three synthetic products just described have different characteristics; therefore a prefix is generally used: viscose rayon; cuprammonium, or Bemberg, rayon; acetate rayon.

Acetate rayon, which is best known by the trade name Celanese, is not chemically related to the viscose types described above. The unpolymerized cellulose molecule, $C_6H_{10}O_5$, seems to contain in its structure three hydroxyl groups. While not an alcohol, it behaves much like one, and is capable of forming an ester with an acid: with acetic acid it can form cellulose triacetate, $C_6H_7O_5(COCH_3)_3$. Actually the cellulose and the ester are highly polymerized. The cellulose will not esterify with acetic acid, even if of 100 per cent strength, because water, which is set free just as soon as reaction begins, slows down combination and eventually stops it. Strong sulphuric acid cannot be employed to hold this water, for it would decompose both the cellulose and the acetic acid. Therefore the esterfying mixture used is 100 per cent (glacial) acetic acid plus acetic anhydride, that is, acetic acid from which the water-forming equivalents have been removed:

$$2\,CH_3COOH = (CH_3CO)_2O + H_2O$$

In the esterification of the cellulose, the acetic anhydride takes up the water as fast as it forms, to re-form acetic acid.

The cellulose acetate is not carried quite to the triacetate stage. (Should it be, the product is given a long boiling with water to decompose a part of it.) The properly prepared acetate is soluble in acetone, CH_3COCH_3, which may be made from acetic acid, or obtained as a by-product of the fermentation of glucose to butyl alcohol. The acetone solution of the acetate is squirted through a spinneret to form filaments, and the solvent acetone is evaporated and recovered for use again. Acetate rayon is just a little harsher to the hand than the other rayons, but has much greater strength when wet, and a somewhat higher luster. It melts at a low temperature, and therefore must be ironed with care. With a very dense structure, this fiber has a small capacity to absorb color, and requires special dyes.

The newest synthetic textile fiber is Nylon, which does not contain cellulose. It is the result of ten years of research and development. Like wool and silk, it is an amino compound. It is a highly polymerized compound, with a molecular weight well above 20,000, and a most unique molecular structure. Nylon is made by condensation of two organic products belonging to the aliphatic series, each of the two a chain compound having the property of being reactive at each end of the chain. Polymerization of such a compound can continue linearly to great lengths of molecule. The raw materials are adipic acid, $HOOC(CH_2)_4COOH$, and hexamethylenediamine, $H_2N(CH_2)_6NH_2$. The product of the reaction is probably hexamethylene adipamide, $—NH(CH_2)_6NHOC(CH_2)_4CO—$, this repeated in chainlike linkage to form the desired polymer, Nylon.

The production of the base substances for Nylon is typical of the work of the synthetic organic chemist. The prime consideration was that the raw materials had to be easily available.

Hexamethylenediamine had never been produced commercially, and in fact was mentioned only in the most exhaustive of organic textbooks. Adipic acid had been made in small amount from castor oil, which is imported and not too plentiful. The ultimate solution of the raw-material problem lay in phenol, either extracted from coal tar or made synthetically from benzol, which is first transformed to adipic acid in a two-step operation. The phenol is melted, then charged into a closed pressure vessel with a catalyst consisting of finely divided nickel; hydrogen is introduced under pressure and reacts with the phenol to form cyclohexanol, $C_6H_{11}OH$, an alcohol. The reaction:

$$C_6H_5OH + 3\ H_2 = C_6H_{11}OH$$

This is oxidized directly to adipic acid, with air and a catalyst, or with a strong oxidizing agent like nitric acid. The reaction:

$$C_6H_{11}OH + 2\ O_2 = HOOC(CH_2)_4COOH + H_2O$$

This is an example of the transformation of an aromatic or ring compound, phenol, to an aliphatic or chain compound, adipic acid.

The raw material chosen for the production of hexamethylenediamine is adipic acid as made by the method described. In its further transformation, the adipic is first neutralized with ammonia to form ammonium adipate, $NH_4OOC(CH_2)_4COONH_4$. This adipate is then heated to decomposition, water being evolved in its transformation to tetramethylene adipamine:

$$NH_4OOC(CH_2)_4COONH_4 = H_2NOC(CH_2)_4CONH_2 + 2\ H_2O$$

The final step in the preparation is to reduce the adipamine to hexamethylenediamine by hydrogen—replacing the oxygen with hydrogen.

With these two intermediates, the production of Nylon consists in combining the adipic acid and the diamine to an ester. This is then polymerized into the long chain structure by heating to a high temperature under an atmosphere of nitrogen, in an autoclave. Here it is kept under most careful control to insure the correct degree of molecular aggregation, so that successive batches are as near alike as possible. The molten product from the autoclave is extruded as a ribbon, and received on a rotating chilled wheel, where it is quickly cooled to white glasslike flakes. The flakes are further broken into small chips, and lots from many batches are again blended in a melting kettle to insure the maximum of uniformity. After filtering, the molten mass is forced through a spinneret. The fine filaments set as they cool, and are then stretched to about four times their original length, this enormously increasing their strength, which exceeds that of any other textile fiber. Nylon also has great elasticity, stretching about 25 per cent before breaking. Since the melting point of the product is around 450° Fahrenheit, fabrics made from it can be washed and ironed without difficulty.

Two synthetic fibers have important industrial application, but are used only for novelties in the clothing field. Vinyon is a fiber made from 88 to 90 per cent vinyl chloride, $CH_2:CHCl$, and 10 to 12 per cent vinyl acetate, $CH_3COOCH:CH_2$. The two compounds are mixed and, under the influence of a catalyst, polymerize together to a molecular weight of above 20,000. In this form Vinyon is a white fluffy powder, which is dissolved in acetone and spun into filament, like cellulose acetate, and with the same equipment. This filament, or yarn twisted from it, is comparatively weak, and is stretched to two or three times the original length, and "set" by heating under tension to about 200°. The fiber is resistant to both acids and alkalies, and is used to make filter cloth. It is quite water-repellent and has been made into fishlines, leaders, and nets, for it is remarkably strong. It cannot be heated above 150°, too low a temperature for safe washing and ironing, and is not recommended for garments that require laundering.

Another synthetic fiber is Fiberglass, a true spun glass. The glass is prepared in the usual manner from limestone, soda, and potash, and is molded into small marbles which, after careful inspection and sorting, are remelted in an electric furnace. The molten glass is allowed to drip out through a hole in the bottom of the furnace. It is picked up by a jet of high-pressure air, which tears it apart and blows it into fibers eight to twelve inches long. These are caught on a belt, given a lose twist to form a roving, and spun into yarn. The molten glass from the electric furnace may also be pressed through a spinneret as a continuous filament. In spinning and weaving, Fiberglass must be coated with a sizing material to protect both the thread and the textile equipment. Starch and vegetable oil compositions are used for this, because they are readily removed from the finished article by soap and hot water.

Being a true glass, this synthetic is not affected by water, most acids, or weak alkalies, and is absolutely fireproof. It is used in the electrical industry for insulation, wrapping, braid, as woven tapes, sleeves, and tying cords. It can be woven on any standard loom, Jacquards included, and is made into damasks, brocades, and taffetas for hangings, drapes, awnings, and tablecloths. It is proof against smudge, stain, mildew, insects, and cigarette burns. It cannot be dyed, but color added in the glass furnace becomes a part of the fiber.

Saran, an ethyl cellulose, has not been made into filament, but in coarser form has been used for woven car-seat covering, also for trimmings and the like. Its principal use is for mechanical goods.

Inventors have long sought to eliminate the operations of spining, weaving, and knitting. The viscose solution can be sheeted, as is proven by cellophane. It is hoped that some day a finished garment can be fabricated in a single operation. Instead of being sewed, the pieces would be joined by adhesive, or by welding. So far only certain types of work clothes and bathing suits have resulted, for the soft textures and graceful drape of woven and knitted fabrics are lacking. These properties depend on the pliable thread or yarn made up of a multiplicity of fine filaments. A raincoat has been made, but not a lounging robe or evening gown.

The synthetic fibers have been greatly improved since the first introduction of the pyroxylin silk. Strength, water resistance, ability to take dyes presented difficult problems to the chemist, now rather happily solved. The amino types, of which Nylon is representative, are more elastic than natural silk and wear better; yet they are only in their infancy. The days of the foreign silk monopoly are forever ended.

These synthetic fibers are typical of a phase of economic life not commonly understood. Natural products are rarely of uniform quality, for they are influenced greatly by conditions surrounding their growth: climate, temperature, rainfall, disease, and pest. Nature may be a low-cost worker, but she is a poor grader. Highly mechanized industry must operate on rigorously standardized raw materials. Here the synthetic product is supreme, for all operations are under rigid control. Where there is elaborate processing in conversion to a consumer product, the higher cost of the synthetic may not be a handicap, being more than made up in the cost of subsequent processing. If the synthetic product has marked superiority over the natural, the later has lost its place in our economy, for the universal history of synthetic production is a continuing lower cost. The chemist is making more history in the days to come than the army or the politician.

Chapter IX

PULP AND PAPER

Though paper is not considered as one of the primary necessities of life, it is difficult to conceive of living without it: It is part of our homes as builder's paper, wallboard, wallpaper; it packages many of our foods; and with it we diffuse knowledge, keep our records, and pay our debts. Politicians owe a great deal to paper; without it their demagogic utterances would rarely get beyond the sound of their voices.

The first artist drew his crude pictures on the walls of his cave. The early writers used a smooth surface of sand, later a clay tablet, or engraved on stone for their permanent record. The precursor of paper was made by the Egyptians from the paper reed, or papyrus plant, which grows in shallow water to a height of twelve to fifteen feet. The stem is about two inches in diameter, hollow, and filled with pith.

Papyrus was made by splitting the middle portion of a stem into several pieces, removing the pith, and flattening out the rounded sections. Such strips were laid side by side to the width desired, and cross strips were interwoven, to form a very coarse textile or mat. After long soaking in water, the mat was laid on a flat surface and hammered with a broad-faced mallet. This stretched the strips so that they overlapped and stuck together. Widths varied from four to eighteen inches, the majority being nine to twelve. Whether an adhesive was used or reliance was placed solely on the natural gums of the plant, is not now quite clear. But an adhesive was used to attach one sheet to another, forming the roll or scroll.

The earliest examples of papyrus date from the sixth century B.C., but the art was much older. It spread over all the eastern Mediterranean and persisted until paper replaced it around the eighth century of the Christian Era.

In the second century B.C. parchment, or vellum, began to compete with papyrus. It was made from the skins of young animals—lambs, goats, and calves. Later, mature sheepskins were used for a second-grade parchment. There are no good accounts of the earliest method of making parchment; but it differed from the later practice.

The skins were washed, limed, and dehaired, thoroughly scraped, and again thoroughly washed to remove all lime. The soft wet skins were then stretched tightly on a frame. All rough spots were scraped and rubbed smooth, and the skins were polished on both sides with chalk and pumice. Much later a method of bleaching was introduced, and very white sheets appeared about the tenth century after Christ. Neither papyrus nor parchment could ever have met the demands of printing in even its earliest days. Fortunately, long before the invention of the printing press, paper as we now know it was available in quantity.

Paper may be defined as a matted or felted sheet of cellulose fiber, more or less filled with a miscellaneous variety of materials, and chemically treated to impart qualities in keeping with its subsequent use.

The Chinese made paper before the Christian Era, and some of the Chinese paper seems to have found its way into Arabia about the eighth century; but western Asia and Europe do not seem to have practiced the art much before the twelfth century. All early paper was made from flax or from linen rags.

The rags for paper making were thoroughly washed and beaten to a fine smooth pulp, and screened to remove any coarse material. This pulp was poured into a tub of water and diluted to a concentration of only 2 or 3 per cent. A fine wire screen of the size of the sheet to be made, provided with a removable wooden frame. was dipped into the well stirred tub, the submergence depending on the thickness of the sheet to be made. It caught a certain amount of pulp on the screen as it was lifted out of the tub. When above the surface of the liquid, the screen and its load of pulp was given a peculiar sidewise motion, in two directions, which felted the cellulose fibers as the water drained out through the mesh. It was then turned upside down and placed on a pad of wool-felt. The frame was removed, and the wire cloth carefully stripped off the sheet. Another piece of wool-felt was laid on top of the paper, and the operation repeated to form a pile of alternating felt and paper. The whole pile was then put into a press, and as much water as possible squeezed out. The pile was then torn apart, and the paper spread to dry under light pressure. The sheets were sized in a bath of gelatine, or glue, and alum solution, to give them strength and improve the water resistance. This early paper was usually water-marked by laying a design on the wire screen, which reduced the thickness of the sheet at the point of contact.

Small hand paper mills spread all over Europe and America. There were two hundred in the United States around 1800. Hand-made paper is still produced in the same way, always from linen or cotton rags.

Today, most paper is made by machine. The chemist is concerned only with the production of the raw materials and the finishing. It is almost impossible to list all the many varieties and qualities of paper now in common use. The raw materials are rags, wood, esparto, hemp, jute, straw, and manila—in fact almost anything that yields a cellulose fiber.

For the high-grade papers used for our money, and any purpose requiring strength and permanency, rags are the raw material, Linen rags give the strongest fiber, but are less plentiful than cotton. The rags are carefully sorted as to kind and color before delivery to the paper mill. At the mill they are again sorted, and all foreign matter—buttons, metal, rubber, sticks, and stones—is carefully picked out. After final inspection they are cut into small pieces by drawing them across the blade of a knife fixed vertically on the sorting table. They are then charged into boilers, either stationary or rotating, and cooked with live steam under pressure for six to eight hours. Caustic soda, or soda ash and lime, is added to help remove grease, dirt, textile sizings, and the like. After cooking, the batch is drained and thoroughly rinsed with water.

The cooked rags are then disintegrated in the "beater," or "hollander." This is an open tank, oval in shape, some twenty feet long, eight feet wide, and three feet deep, with a partition down the middle, the "mid-feather," parallel to the straight sides, and short of reaching the ends. Between the partition and one side wall is a heavy roll, four to five feet in diameter, with steel knives set in its circumference and parallel to its axis. The roller is carried on bearings which can be accurately adjusted as to height. It is rotated by a belt and pulley. Under the roll is a bed plate made of steel bars bolted together, and set parallel to the knives on the roll. The rotating roll acts as a paddle wheel and circulates the stock around the trough of the beater, so that all must pass between the knives on the roll and the bed plate. Clean water is continuously added, and the dirty water taken off through a revolving screen that holds back the rags and fiber. The roll is slowly lowered, thus giving more and more cutting action, and eventually reduces the rags to a thin pulp.

If bleaching is required, it is usually performed in the beater, with a solution of sodium hypochlorite, $NaClO$, made from caustic soda and chlorine. When the stock is white enough, it is thoroughly washed in the beater, by adding fresh water. Next it is "sized" with a crude sodium abietate, $(CH_3)_2CH(CH_3)_2C_{14}H_{16}COONa$, or rosin soap, prepared in advance from rosin and alkali. After thorough incorporation of this size in the pulp, aluminum sulphate is added to precipitate the rosin on the cellulose fiber as an insoluble aluminum abietate.

Sizing is a very delicate operation, yet one of the utmost importance, for it influences markedly the quality of the paper. The size not only acts as a binder in the finished paper, thus adding strength, but determines how absorbent the paper will be of water and of ink. It must be applied uniformly, so that no rosin specks or stains are produced in the finished paper.

To make a paper particularly water-resistant, large quantities of free rosin are put into the size. Various waxes may be used for this same purpose. Recently a synthetic resin has produced paper that has unusual strength, even when wet.

To secure opacity, a mineral substance—China clay or kaolin—is added to the paper stock while in the beater.

From the beater, the stock is passed through the Jordan engine, sometimes several times. This machine consists of a conical shell made up of alternate steel bars and oak staves. A closely fitting runner of the same construction is accurately centered in bearings, so that it may be rotated inside the shell. This reduces the paper stock to the desired fiber length; and after passing through screens that take out all coarse material it goes to storage and thence to the paper machine.

The largest production of paper is from wood. A semifinished product called wood pulp, or simply pulp, is first manufactured. Pulp is merely a refined cellulose fiber, sometimes bleached, but not sized, and it is shipped to the paper mills and other users of pulp for further treatment. Only the larger paper mills make both pulp and paper. The pulp, after manufacture, is formed into thick sheets, dried, and packed into bales. The various processes of making pulp are designed for use with different varieties of wood, and to give a material suitable for papers of widely differing qualities.

The *mechanical process* for making pulp employs little chemistry. Green wood, preferably spruce, is the most suitable raw material. The spruce is cut to length, the bark removed by hand or machine, all charred spots cut out, and it is then sent to the grinders. In these machines the logs are driven end-on, under heavy pressure from a hydraulic cylinder, against a rapidly revolving grindstone. The operation develops great heat, and the stone must be kept flooded with water, which also serves to float away the ground wood. This is screened to remove coarse pieces, and is run to a beater for further disintegration. It is bleached like the rag stock, and then is fed to the "wet machine"—a trough in which a rotating screen covered with 60-mesh screen cloth revolves. This screen is so arranged in a tub that the pulp adheres to the outside surface, while the water runs through the screen and out. A coarse woolen felt, or "blanket," is held against the pulp layer by a pressure (couch) roller, and the pulp sticks to the felt, which carries it away. The blanket and its layer of pulp passes between successive rollers of a long series that squeeze out some of the water. The last roller of the series is of hard wood, and this takes the pulp off the felt. When thick enough, the sheet is cut and stripped from the roller, passes to a cutter, and is baled, or sent to the paper mill.

The *soda process*, in which caustic soda extracts the sap, gum, lignin, etc., is used to produce pulp from poplar and similar woods. The timber is felled, cut to length, and air-dried for a year or more. To remove the bark, a number of logs are rotated in a cage under water, wearing it off as they rub together. After the black knots and charred wood have been cut out, the logs are sent to the "chipper," which shaves them into chips about a quarter of an inch thick and an inch square. The chips are screened to remove saw-dust and oversized pieces.

The chips are charged into heavy steel pressure cookers, fifty feet high and ten feet in diameter, which digest them for ten or more hours in a solution containing about 6 per cent caustic soda, and at a steam pressure of some ninety to one hundred pounds per square inch. At the end of the cooking, still under the steam pressure, a large valve in the bottom of the cooker is opened, through which the contents are shot out into a receiving tank. This violent discharge smashes the chips to a pulpy mass. The pulp is separated from the cooking liquors, washed with water, and sent to beaters for complete disintegration.

The liquors are saved, evaporated to dryness, and the residue burned in a rotary kiln to eliminate the tar, gums, and other organic materials extracted from the wood. The burning produces a "black ash" which is mostly carbonate of soda, and can be converted to caustic soda by treatment with lime, just as in the production of caustic (Chapter V), which in turn may be used over again in the decomposition of more wood.

Soda pulp is always yellow and must be bleached, for its principal use is in high-grade book, magazine, and writing papers. The pulp is sheeted in the same manner as mechanical pulp. Soda pulp makes a soft spongy paper that, when carefully bleached, does not deteriorate with age.

Sulphite pulp is usually made from spruce, and in the same manner as soda pulp up to the cooking stage. Then the chips are cooked in a mixture of calcium sulphite, $CaSO_3$, magnesium sulphite, $MgSO_3$, and free sulphurous acid, H_2SO_3. Since this is acid, the digesters must be lined with acid-proof material such as vitrified tile. The sulphite solution is made by burning sulphur to sulphur dioxide, SO_2, which is cooled and then passed through a tall wooden tower filled with the mineral dolomite, $CaCO_3 \cdot MgCO_3$; through it a stream of water trickles to dissolve the sulphites as fast as they are formed.

The time of cooking varies: the slower the cooking, the stronger the fiber. The sulphurous acid has a strong bleaching action, and this pulp is very light-colored.

The cooking liquors are separated from the pulp by screening, and the pulp very thoroughly washed; for any liquors left in it will cause the fiber gradually to darken and loses strength and flexibility. The pulp is carefully screened to remove undigested wood and coarse fiber, and then goes to the wet mill for sheeting. Before being converted into paper, the sulphite pulp is given a hard beater treatment, followed by the Jordan.

Because of its great strength, sulphite pulp can be diluted with a large amount of mechanical pulp. For newsprint the stock sometimes carries as low as 5 per cent sulphite blended with 95 per cent mechanical pulp. Even at this dilution such stock can be converted into paper on machines operating at 1,200 feet per minute. Sulphite pulp is also a blending material for printing and writing papers, and was for a long time the most important of the chemical pulps.

The sulphate process is a late-comer, and is particularly adapted to the conversion of coniferous wood into pulp. No other process can deal with its high rosin content. Sulphate mills are scattered through the Gulf States where they use southern pine.

Although called the sulphate process because the raw material used in making the cooking liquor is sodium sulphate, or salt cake, Na_2SO_4, the actual decomposition is effected by a solution of sodium sulphide, Na_2S, and caustic soda. The resulting pulp and paper is called kraft pulp and kraft paper, because of its great strength. It is largely used for wrapping paper, bags, boxes, and containers. New methods of bleaching that do not reduce the strength of the finished product make light-colored pulps possible, and a really white pulp will be ready after the war.

The operation of the kraft process is the same as that of the soda process. The rosin content of the pine wood is converted into a rosin soap by the alkali, and is recovered from the digestion as "black liquor." It is separated from the pulp, and is evaporated to dryness and fused in a furnace, the organic matter present furnishing the fuel and at the same time a reducing agent to convert sulphate to sulphide. Fresh salt cake is added before furnacing to make up for processing losses (about 250 pounds per ton of pulp).

A product similar to turpentine is recovered from the vapors that come out of the top of the digesters in modern kraft mills. After purification this is used as a raw material for synthetic camphor. The black liquor from the digesters is actually a complex sodium soap of rosin, stearic and oleic acids. It can be clarified and used by the laundry-soap industry.

This process is very economical not only of chemical reagents, but also of wood. Whereas it takes forty years to reproduce a stand of timber in northern woods, a mere dozen suffices for southern pine.

The conversion of pulp into paper is mechanical, and is much the same for all varieties of paper. A modern paper machine produces a continuous sheet, up to twenty feet wide, and of a length limited only by convenience in handling. The machine consists of two main parts, called the "wet end," and the "dry end." The former carries an endless wire screen on two suspended driving rolls, called the "Fourdrinier," which operates at speeds above 1,000 feet per minute; and the speed of the screen determines the rate of production. The screen and all its appurtenances are carried by a cradle, which oscillates at right angles to the direction of travel. A rubber band on each side of the screen determines the width of paper. Above the screen is a distributing box, which spreads the thin stream of pulp suspended in water, evenly across the entire width of the screen cloth.

This pulp is made from appropriate mixtures of the several varieties, has been thoroughly mixed in the beater, bleached, treated with the sizing materials, and contains the mineral filler. All chemical operations have been completed before it reaches the machine, even to the dyeing, if colored papers are to be made.

As the pulp flows on the Fourdrinier, the surplus water runs through, leaving a thin film of pulp, which is matted by the shaking motion. The matted pulp passes over suction boxes which draw off more of the water, and then between squeezing rolls. A "dandy roller" impresses the watermark on quality paper. At the last pressure roll the paper is dry enough to stick, abandoning the wire, which returns to the head end of the machine.

From this roll the paper is detached and sent to the "dry end." Here it passes up and down, and in and out, through highly polished, steam-heated rolls, which evaporate the remaining water. Finally the sheet passes the trimmer to the reel that forms the finished roll of paper ready for the market. Some modern machines have as many as sixty drying rolls. For some varieties of paper a light taut felt travels part way through the dry end with the paper to support it and prevent tearing.

Printed illustrations require paper with a glossy finish. For this, the paper is sent through a "calender"—a set of highly polished, vertically mounted heavy rolls, each in contact with its neighbors, sometimes heated by steam. Their pressure as the paper passes between successive rolls produces the glossy surface. For a very glossy surface, the paper is coated (either by dipping or by brushing) with mineral products mixed with casein to make them adhere. Chalk, soapstone, blanc fixe (barium sulphate), and satin white (calcium aluminate) are the commonly used coating materials.

Waste paper is an important raw material for carton and box boards. The waste from the paper mills and cutters can be shredded and returned to beaters for disintegration. Newspapers contain an ink which has a carbon pigment that cannot be bleached by any available chemical reagent. A part can be removed mechanically from the beater pulp, but most of it remains and makes the pulp gray.

For the heavier boards a slow-running paper machine is used, with several distributing boxes that feed different formulations of pulp successively on the wire. This builds up a composite sheet of a thickness regulated by the rate of feeding and the speed of the wire. Thick wallboard is made on a batch machine which produces a sheet of the exact dimensions desired. Some wallboard is made of several layers of heavy paper, glued together.

Corrugated paper is composed of several layers (one crimped), pasted together with water glass (sodium silicate) solution.

Many special objects are made of paper by dipping a perforated mold into a suspension of pulp in water. The form is connected to a vacuum pump which sucks the water through the perforations, which stop the pulp as a thin covering layer. This is blown off the form by a blast of compressed air. The cone of the radio loudspeaker is made in this manner, and requires successive formation from three or four varieties of pulp. Protective shields for bottle packing are made in the same manner.

Vulcanized fiber is made from unsized paper. The sheet is passed continuously through a bath of zinc chloride, $ZnCl_2$, and rolled up on a large drum under the pressure of a smooth roll resting on it. The sheet is cut off and flattened under pressure. Small round rods, ferrules, and tubes are rolled on a mandrel. The zinc chloride solution contains about 60 per cent of the salt and is used hot. It gelatinizes the surface of the paper, causing welding, but must be completely washed out of the fiber before drying. The washing is a long slow operation, requiring several months for a piece an inch thick. The finished product is hard and hornlike, and is used extensively for electrical insulation.

Parchment paper is made by treating unsized paper in a 70 per cent sulphuric acid solution for a very short time. It is immediately washed in water until the last trace of acid is removed, and dried under tension or slight pressure.

Waxed papers are made of rag stock, and coated by passing through a bath of molten paraffine.

The better grades of tissue papers are made of rag stock, beaten to extreme fineness; the lower grades use a sulphite stock. Cigarette paper is made of flax and requires very pure water for its manufacture. Blotting paper, and paper towels and cleaning tissue, are soda or sulphite products without size or filler. The safety bank-check paper is a sulphite base, chemically treated to make altera-tions on its surface easily detectable.

The increasing use of paper containers instead of wooden boxes, or of imported jute bags, has presented some complex chemical problems. Ordinary paper loses its strength when wet and disinte-grates. New types of size, using synthetic resins that are water-insoluble when cured, has helped. New waterproof adhesives have improved the multi-walled bag so that it can hold damp materials. Ammunition is now packed in paper cartons, after a protective sleeve of formed pulp has been slipped over the shells. These are emergency developments that will be of application in normal times.

Because it takes so long for trees to grow, the paper industry is ever searching for new raw materials. Waste farm products like straw and cornstalks have attracted the paper chemist, but so far they have been of very limited use in the paper industry. The chemist has solved the problem of converting them; but gathering the vast tonnages required by a commercial paper mill, and storing such bulky materials, is uneconomical in the United States in com-petition with wood.

The uniform quality of paper—in texture, thickness of sheet, color, freedom from imperfections—is taken as a matter of course. Actually it is the result of most careful selection of raw mate-rials, seemingly endless disintegration (beating and Jordaning), thorough washing with enormous quantities of clean water. Paper-making is a fine art, and there are ever new applications for its many products and varieties.

Transparent films, such as celluloid, cellophane, tenite, and pliofilm, do not belong in the category of paper, even though some of them are made of cellulose. Cellophane is similar to viscose rayon: the cellulose solution has plasticizer added before sheeting. Tenite is cellulose acetate in sheet form instead of filament. Several of the films are vinyl compounds similar to the base from which Vinyon is made; others are rubber derivatives.

ELECTROLYTIC CAUSTIC SODA AND CHLORINE CELLS

Left bank operating; right bank under construction

MODERN OIL REFINERY

Producing field and tank farm in background—14,000 barrels crude
cracked per day

Chapter X

SOAP AND DETERGENTS

Cleanliness, despite all appearances, really seems to be an attribute of the human race. It is practiced by the most primitive peoples of all the continents. The Indian of Central America makes a daily pilgrimage to the watercourse for a bath and hour of gossip. In Africa the natives working in the mines will set up a makeshift shower. The peasant on the steppes takes a steam bath in midwinter, finishing with a roll in the snowbank. But water alone is not the perfect cleansing agent, and if hard (from contact with limestone), is a most unsatisfactory dirt remover.

Dirt adheres to our bodies because it is almost always associated with some form of oil or grease. A vegetable oil, acting as a flushing agent, probably was the earliest detergent, or cleanser.

The use of such alkaline materials as sodium and potassium carbonates in dirt removal began before written history. But these compounds are rather harsh to the human skin. It is not known when man learned to relieve their harshness by combining them with vegetable oils and animal fats to make soaps; but it was long before the Christian Era.

Common though soap is today, no one knows exactly just how it functions in cleaning. The chemist defines soap as a metallic salt of a fatty acid. If the metal is sodium or potassium (rarely ammonium), the soap is the familiar one of the household or the factory. Such soaps are slightly soluble in water. But other metals also make soaps, which are not at all soluble in water and have no cleansing power. Aluminum soaps are waterproofing agents, used to treat textiles such as tarpaulins, tent fabrics, ducks, and raincoats. Other soaps are made from lead, or from manganese, and are used to hasten the drying of paints. Some calcium and aluminum soaps are used to make lubricating greases.

The vegetable oils and animal fats from which the ordinary soaps are made are esters of glycerol (glycerine), and one or more fatty acids (see page 47). Glycerine is a trihydric alcohol; that is, it contains three hydroxyl groups. The fatty acids are monobasic; that is, they have only one replaceable hydrogen. The oil or fat therefore contains one molecule of glycerine to three molecules of the fatty acid. Mineral oils, being hydrocarbons, do not make soap. If the oil or fat is treated with caustic soda, the strong alkali displaces the weakly attached glycerine in the combination and sets it free. The alkali, in turn, combines with the fatty acid to form a sodium salt— soap. In the case of tallow, a stearate, the reaction is:

$$C_{17}H_{35}COOCH_2$$
$$|$$
$$C_{17}H_{35}COOCH + 3\,NaOH = 3\,C_{17}H_{36}COONa + C_3H_5(OH)_3$$
$$|$$
$$C_{17}H_{35}COOCH_2$$

      stearate   caustic   soap   glycerine

The chemist calls it "saponification."

The choice of the oil is largely a matter of cost and the use for which the soap is intended. Palm oils, coconut oil, olive oil, whale and fish oils, tallow, lard, all are used. They contain various proportions of three fatty acids: stearic acid, $C_{17}H_{35}COOH$; palmitic acid, $C_{15}H_{31}COOH$; oleic acid, $C_{17}H_{33}COOH$. These three are by far the most common of the soap bases. Another fatty acid, found in rosin and called abietic acid, $C_{19}H_{29}COOH$, also combines with caustic soda to form a sodium salt, and rosin is often put into household soaps.

When these sodium and potassium esters, or soaps, are dissolved in hard water, they precipitate the calcium salts present, forming insoluble lime soaps. The curd that separates out usually picks up loosened dirt and forms the scum that sticks to the bathtub, the so-called soap ring. This limitation is inherent in ordinary soaps, and is a real problem in the fine laundering of white goods, for the curd adheres to the textile, giving it a dark color, and is very difficult to remove by rinsing. Therefore most laundries use softened water—

from which the calcium salts have been removed. The calcium salts that produce the "hardness" of hard water are precipitated first with soap; then a further addition of soap forms lather and performs its real task of loosening the dirt. The soap saved in laundries using softened water pays for the cost of water treatment, and the finished wash has a better color besides.

Dirt is nearly always accompanied by grease or oil, of which there are abundant sources, such as spilled food, contact with greasy objects, and the automobile exhaust. Soap emulsifies grease and oil—that is, it breaks the grease and oil into extremely fine drops, which mix with the soapy water and remain suspended in it; then the grease and oil can be floated away from the dirt, and this can be rinsed out.

In machine shops, oils and greases are used to lubricate, to facilitate drilling and machining, and to prevent rust. Coatings of oil must be removed from machine parts before painting or enameling if this is to serve its purpose. Grease is removed from fine and intricate parts with such solvents as organic chlorides (see page 43). Industrial soaps are used for cleaning most heavy machine parts. These shop soaps contain a great deal of free alkali, and relatively little actual soap—just enough to assist in the rinsing; they are quite different from the toilet and laundry soaps of the household.

There are many ways of making soap. The fatty constituent is usually a blend of many materials. In toilet soaps of the better grades, they are usually olive, palm, and coconut oils. Household and laundry soaps use various mixtures of tallow, waste greases, rosin and fish oils, the mixture being determined largely by economic conditions in the oil and grease markets. Industrial soaps for laundries and textile mills use tallow and olive oil. Soaps made with soda alkali are hard, those with potash, soft, and the latter may be put into alcohol solution—the liquid soaps. Toilet soaps should contain a slight excess of fat, this excess being in a free state and dispersed through the soap. Some of the industrial soaps contain more alkali than can be combined with the fat, and in consequence are quite caustic.

In the modern soap factory the fats and oils forming the "soap stock" are put, in the desired proportions, into a melting tank and blended into a homogeneous mass. The water and coarse dirt settle out to the bottom.

For light-colored soaps, the melted stock may be bleached, usually with sodium bichromate, $Na_2Cr_2O_7$, and a small amount of hydrochloric acid. In the case of stocks which do not respond to this treatment, a little fuller's earth (a claylike mineral) or a bit of decolorizing carbon (a special porous charcoal) is thoroughly stirred into the liquid fat. The mass is then filtered to remove the decolorizing agents, which have picked up the coloring matter originally present in the fat.

The molten stock goes from the melting tank to the soap pan, where steam is introduced directly into the liquid to boil it. A solution of caustic soda is then run in slowly, and the boiling is continued to thoroughly mix the fat and caustic. The caustic solution added may contain from 10 to 30 per cent active caustic: the soapmaker determines the exact amount to be added by quick test, a little short of the fat equivalent for toilet soaps, a little excess for household soaps. When the reaction as described on page 120 is complete, great quantities of common salt, sodium chloride, are shoveled into the soap kettle, and the boiling is stopped. The salt causes the soap to separate as a curd, and the glycerine and water (now a brine) settle under the layer of soap. The glycerine-brine mixture is drawn off the bottom of the pan, leaving the soap behind. The soap curd is given several water washes to take out any adhering brine.

In the better grades of soap, this washing is most thoroughly done, even to the extent of boiling the soap curd with each water addition. The wash water is held to a minimum, as it is all run to storage for recovery of any glycerine it may contain. Finally the soap is again melted and left to cool and settle. It separates into two layers, a good grade of "settled soap" and an underlayer of "nigre" —a lower grade, since it contains some impurities and more entrained water. If it is a toilet soap, the settled soap is carefully separated and sent to the finishing department, where dyes and perfumes are added, and the mass is thoroughly stirred, or "crutched," to give it a smooth homogeneous texture. The nigre is batched with a soap of lower quality.

All varieties of soap are crutched at a temperature just above the melting point, and then cast into large slabs. After cooling, the slabs are sliced into bars which are given a light drying to harden their surfaces, and then cut into rectangular pieces and pressed into the usual cakes. In some highly mechanized plants, the crutched soap is extruded into a continuous bar, which runs through a continuous dryer, and to the cutter and press.

All scrap around the plant is put back into the nigre, melted, and given another treatment with salt. It is finally worked up into a lower-grade soap.

Household laundry soaps often contain rosin. The rosin is cooked with soda ash, and the solution added to the crutchers. Other addition agents are often used, some as fillers, others to precipitate lime and save soap; and still others have limited detergent properties. Clays are used as fillers; sodium carbonate, sodium silicate, and borax have water-softening and detergent properties. These are added as solids in the crutching operation.

Glycerine is a very valuable by-product of soap manufacture, and efforts have been made to increase the yield and simplify the recovery.

The oils and fats that make up soap stocks can be split into fatty acid and glycerine by the use of water and a catalytic agent—naphthalene-oleic-sulphonic acid (made by treating naphthalene and oleic acid with very strong sulphuric acid). The molten soap stock, usually of low-grade materials such as garbage grease and residues from vegetable oil refining, is put into a large open tank and boiled with live steam. It is washed with very dilute sulphuric acid, followed by water. The catalytic agent—to the weight of 1 per cent of the stock—is then added, and very slow boiling is resumed for about a day. The fat splits into fatty acid and glycerine. The glycerine dissolves in water condensed during the boiling, settles to the bottom, and is drawn off as a 15 per cent solution. The splitting is complete, and the glycerine is not contaminated by salt, nor diluted by wash water.

The fatty acid is converted into soap by treatment with sodium carbonate, caustic soda not being required for conversion of the fatty acid.

Soap powders are mixtures of soap and soda ash, made by mixing molten soap with the ash in a powerful beater. The mixture contains 35 to 40 per cent water, and is grained by forcing it through a screen. Scouring soaps and powders contain a coarse to fine grit such as ground pumice; in the most widely advertised of these ground feldspar is the abrasive. Soap chips are made by squeezing between heavy rolls, and drying. Soap beads are made by spraying molten soap in a tall tower; it freezes into small hollow spheres as it falls. Floating soaps are agitated in the crutching operation in such a way that air is beaten into the mass of the soap. They contain about 30 per cent water, as contrasted with 10 per cent in ordinary hard soaps. The industrial textile soaps used to level dyes and soften fabrics are potash soaps, carefully formulated to contain no free alkali. In medicated soaps, cresol, sulphur, thymol, mercury salts, etc., are added in the crutching operation, just before casting into slabs or molds.

The textile chemist has been forced to find substitutes for soap. In dyeing, the curd of the calcium soap attaches itself to the fabric and prevents even, or "level," dyeing, and leaves a harsh feel, or "hand," in the cloth. Therefore textile oils (called in the trade "sulphonated oils") are used in place of soap: compounds of various fatty acids and sulphuric acid. They are made from the same varieties of fats and oils as soap (olive oil, castor oil, tallow, etc.), treated with concentrated sulphuric acid in a kettle well agitated and cooled by refrigeration. The chemistry is complex and not well understood, and the processes are largely empirical as to proportions, time, and temperature. These textile oils, which are not good detergents, act by wetting the fiber, thus permitting even penetration of the dye. They also soften the textile. They do not precipitate lime from hard water.

Compounds of quite a different class have been taking the place of sulphonated oils in the detergent field in recent years. They are called wetting agents, because they facilitate the wetting of objects that resist water, and for this purpose they are many times more powerful than soap without precipitating lime from hard waters. Some of them have excellent detergent properties. One, very widely used in shampoos, in tooth powders, and in liquid dentifrices, is a sulphate of lauric alcohol, probably $[CH_3(CH_2)_{11}]_2SO_4$. Lauric alcohol is made by reduction of lauric acid (a constituent of coconut oil) with hydrogen. Another is a complex compound of succinic acid, octyl alcohol, and sodium sulphate.

Caustic soda in solution is used in industrial cleaning, but is too strong for the laundry and household. The milder sodium carbonate, in the form of a hydrated crystal, sal soda, $Na_2CO_3 \cdot 10\ H_2O$, is a safer product. A very mild alkali that is rarely used by itself for cleaning purposes is bicarbonate of soda, $NaHCO_3$, better known as baking soda. The modified sodas are mixtures of carbonate and bicarbonate, which permit the alkali strength to be adjusted to a specific cleaning purpose. Between the strong alkali, caustic soda, and the milder carbonates, is trisodium phosphate, Na_3PO_4, or $Na_3PO_4 \cdot 12\ H_2O$, of which both forms are used in large tonnages. It is the common household cleaning compound called for short "TSP," and sold under many brand names. In strong solution it is also used as a paint remover. All these alkali salts are much cheaper than soap; and properly used, either alone or in combination with soap, they are very effective. They are widely used in the food processing industries, as they leave no taste or odor.

Dry cleaning is anything but dry, though of course no water is used. Very volatile solvents are used to dissolve grease and free the dirt. There are many excellent solvents for grease, but the choice of cleaner is limited to compounds which will not destroy fabrics, including the synthetic fibers, nor discolor whites, nor act on dyes of the most widely varying types and in the most delicate shades.

Highly refined petroleum and coal-tar naphthas were formerly used, but they are extremely inflammable. They have been replaced by several of the chlorinated hydrocarbons: trichlorethylene, $CHCl:CCl_2$; tetrachlorethylene, $CCl_2:CCl_2$; carbon tetrachloride, CCl_4. These are all very volatile liquids and are not inflammable, nor are their vapors explosive.

Clothes are cleaned in these fluids in tightly closed washing machines. The dirty liquids are run off and saved, and a rinse of clean fluids may follow. Any adhering rinse liquid is evaporated by gentle heating. The dirty liquids are sent to distilling apparatus, where the cleaning fluid is vaporized and condensed for reuse, and the dirt left behind in the still. Very compact apparatus, almost automatic in operation, has been developed for carrying out the whole series of manipulations.

While the quality of soap has been greatly improved in recent years, substitutes in increasing numbers are finding increasing application. The substitutes are widely used in the textile mill and in textile finishing. They have a small market in shampoos and dentifrices. It will take a great deal of propaganda to convince a householder that a fraction of an ounce of a liquid or a powder is equivalent to a cake of soap, and will give a much more satisfactory performance. Many of the better substitutes make little lather, which in fact is not at all necessary to cleaning. Thus industry is far ahead of the housewife. The soap ring in the bathtub is not a necessary nuisance, for a soapless powder, containing one of these synthetics, that is on the market may be used in the bath.

Chapter XI

PETROLEUM

Man has ever been a restless creature. His own power of loco motion enables him to travel only a few miles a day in rough country, a little more in flat open regions. Even after animals had been domesticated his speed was but little greater, though the exertion may have been less. Movement by water was equally slow before the advent of the sailing ship, and centuries later the best day's run of Columbus' ships on his four transatlantic voyages, was only two hundred miles, his average day's run much less.

The invention of the steam engine changed all this. Within three generations man was speeding across the country at fifty miles an hour, and crossing the Atlantic in one-third the time the fastest clipper ship required.

The boiler and the engine, their fuel and water, were not too cumbersome for ships and trains, but they were severe limitations for wagons and carriages. There was real need for some form of self-contained transportation unit that could travel the ordinary highway, and be operated by the driver of the team it would replace.

The steam engine had no sooner become a reliable power unit than engineers—a century ago—set out to design an engine that could burn fuel directly in the cylinder, and so do away with the complicated steam generation. Further the steam engine is a rather inefficient unit, in the sense of converting the energy set free in the combustion of fuel into mechanical power.

The invention of the internal combustion engine resulted from this endeavor. These engines are variously called gas, gasoline, oil, or Diesel engines, depending on the type of fuel used, or the method by which the fuel is introduced. The first engines were heavy, complicated, and little suited to transportation requirements. But at the beginning of this century lightweight units of sufficient reliability had been developed, and the automobile became a reality.

Within the past forty years the internal combustion engine has dominated our civilization. By its aid man has conquered the earth, the sea, and the sky.

This type of engine operates only on a liquid or gaseous fuel, the gaseous fuel often being obtained by vaporizing a volatile liquid in a stream of air. The number of such engines built is enormous, in total horsepower far exceeding steam-engine production. In one year a half-billion horsepower of automobile engines alone have been produced; more power generation machinery in a day than is installed at Niagara Falls.

The average automobile engine consumes about three gallons of fuel per hour; the multi-engined military plane a hundred times as much; a great Diesel-driven ocean liner a thousand gallons an hour. All together these oil-driven power generators require an enormous quantity of liquid fuels, all of which is derived from petroleum.

Petroleum has been known for more than two thousand years; its industrial importance began only eighty years ago. In 1940 the United States produced one and a third billion barrels of crude oil —about 60 per cent of the world's output. The barrel of forty-two gallons is the standard of measurement in this country; in Europe, crude and heavy oils are measured in either English or metric tons. The petroleum deposits of the world are not inexhaustible, and already it is necessary to economize. Crude oil must be recovered from the earth at maximum efficiency, and transformed into commercial fuels with maximum output.

Petroleum, or crude oil, is a complex mixture of hundreds, even thousands, of hydrocarbons. Only relatively few have been completely identified. The oils from Pennsylvania contain largely the straight-chain or paraffin hydrocarbons. Those from the Gulf Coast contain, in addition, cyclic paraffins. Oils from Asia contain straight-chain, cyclic, and aromatic hydrocarbons. In addition to the above hydrocarbons, petroleum contains small amounts of various combinations of carbon and hydrogen, with sulphur, nitrogen, and oxygen. The composition varies from field to field, and the oils from various strata, even in the same field, may differ in quality. Olefines are rarely ever present.

Petroleum is always accompanied by natural gas, though the reverse is not true. Natural gas contains the light members of the paraffin series, methane, ethane, and propane. In some fields there is also an appreciable amount of sulphur, combined with the carbon and hydrogen; these sulphur-bearing gases are called "sour."

In a few wells the crude oil consists only of very light hydrocarbons—those containing from four to ten carbon atoms to the molecule. This is almost a natural gasoline. At the other extreme is the asphaltum deposit found on the island of Trinidad, in which there are almost no fluid hydrocarbons. Asphaltum is a highly polymerized naphthene or cyclic hydrocarbon. The Texas and California oils contain large quantities of asphaltum admixed with the lighter naphthenes and paraffins. Since motor fuel is the principal product, and this contains hydrocarbons of four to eight carbon atoms, the lighter petroleums are preferred and bring the higher price.

Petroleum is found at all depths beneath the earth's surface: some fields have producing strata at a depth of only a few hundred feet; others, at depths approaching three miles. In most newly opened fields the oil is under tremendous gas pressures, some of the deeper-lying pools showing three to five thousand pounds per square inch. The gas and oil occur in porous limestones and shales, called "sands." Underneath is frequently found salt brine.

A bore hole is drilled into the oil sands, using a hollow rotating cutting bit. Heavy mud is pumped down through the hollow drill rod to counterbalance the oil and gas pressures as encountered, for otherwise the well would "blow out." Since pressures of thousands of pounds per square inch are encountered in the deeper oil sands, great skill and experience are required to maintain safe hydrostatic balance. The chemist has solved many complex problems of formulation of these drilling muds, and in their maintenance in suitable condition.

Natural gas plays a very important role in oil production. It lifts the oil out of the well. But the solution in the oil underground is of even more importance, for it gives added fluidity, which in turn favors the migration of the oil through the fine interstices of the "sand." After a field has been tapped, gas pressure tends to drop, and it is now common practice to pump gas back into the oil-bearing strata in order to reestablish the gas pressure, which in turn greatly increases the amount of oil that can be brought to the surface before the well is exhausted.

In many fields, the gas coming to the surface with the oil contains appreciable quantities of propane, butane, and pentane. Scrubbing this gas, while under pressure, with a medium heavy oil (usually refrigerated to a temperature below freezing), will dissolve these hydrocarbons in the oil. The rest of the gas passes into the distribution lines. The dissolved hydrocarbons may be driven out of the oil in a still, and condensed. This is the source of the bottled gas used for cooking in country districts, which is propane with a small admixture of butane. The larger part of the butane, the pentane, and higher members of the series are liquids, sold as casing-head gasoline. This, by itself, is too volatile for use in motors; but, blended with refinery gasoline, it gives quick-starting ability. These hydrocarbons are also excellent raw materials for ethylene, and in particular for butadiene, all-important in the production of synthetic rubber.

Crude petroleum has almost no application in its crude state and must be refined. Its various hydrocarbon components boil at different temperatures, and can be separated by distillation, like those of coal tars (see page 64). The following table lists the more common petroleum products, with the number of carbon atoms characteristic of each, and the boiling temperatures (Fahrenheit) at which they come off the still:

Liquefied gas	1 to 4	Below 95°
Petroleum ether	4 to 7	95° to 176°
Gasoline	4 to 12	104° to 390°
Solvents	4 to 14	104° to 425°
Kerosene	10 to 16	347° to 572°
Lubricating oils	20 to 35	Above 660°
Paraffine	23 to 29	. . . .
Asphalt	. . . .	. . . .
Carbon	. . . .	. . . .

The old topping still is a horizontal boiling vessel built over a firebox, and heated by direct flame from oil or gas. A condensing apparatus of pipe is submerged in a water box to cool and liquefy the vapors from the still. By suitable valves, the condensed liquids are turned into successive storage tanks, as the thermometer on the still indicates the finish of distillation of one fraction and the beginning of the next. Complete distillation is rarely carried through in such an apparatus. The common practice is to "top" the crude oil to a temperature of 500°, which produces what is known as *straight-run gasoline.* The residue left in the still is *topped crude,* and finds a market as fuel oil, or is sent to a modern "cracking unit" for conversion to gasoline and other oil fractions by a chemical process to be described later. The yield of straight-run gasoline varies with the quality of the crude oil, and may amount to as much as 30 per cent. About one-third of all gasoline produced is obtained in this way. The kerosene fraction amounts to 10 to 12 per cent of the crude; but this is not now so important as formerly, and much of it comes on the market in the form of furnace oils; No. 1, the lightest, is a crude kerosene; No. 2 contains more of the higher boiling fractions (up to 600°). The Diesel engine fuels consist of fractions boiling up to 700°.

The enormous increase in the demand for motor fuel in the past twenty years could not have been met by straight-run gasoline, first in quantity, second in quality. Some method had to be devised for breaking down the heavier residues into lighter gasoline. The result of research on this problem of getting more gasoline from crude oil is the modern *cracking process,* which, combined with the straight distillation, makes it possible to market 80 per cent of the crude as gasoline.

Cracking in its simplest form is the breaking of the molecules of the heavy and higher hydrocarbons into lighter ones of lower molecular weight. As practiced, the crude oil is first topped to remove the fractions boiling in the range of the gasolines. The heavy residue is then heated under high pressure to temperatures of 750° to 900° Fahrenheit—that is, approaching red heat. Pressures may be up to 1,500 pounds per square inch. The products from the heating unit, both liquid and gaseous, are then released into a vessel, usually at a somewhat lower pressure; here some of the liquids flash into vapor, which then is passed through fractionating columns where the various oil fractions condense out at different levels. These are taken off, cooled, and sent to storage. The heavy residues may be recycled through the process until completely broken down: to gas; to lighter hydrocarbons; to solid carbon if the operation is carried far enough. The process is continuous until stopped by the accumulation of the solid carbon, or coke, in the heating units.

There are many modifications of this process in operation; they operate at different temperatures and pressures, some on liquid oil, some on oil vapor, and with various arrangements of apparatus. The modern cracking still is a most complicated assembly of apparatus, towering more than a hundred feet into the air, with a maze of piping. A single unit may treat 50,000 to 70,000 barrels of crude oil per day, with all operating controls arranged on a board not unlike that of an electrical station. The units are complicated by the necessity of flexibility. In winter less gasoline and more heating oils are called for; in summer, vice versa.

That invaluable assistant of the chemist, the catalyst, has recently found place in the cracking of oils, and most of the new refineries now being built incorporate catalytic cracking in their design. The refiner calls them "cat crackers," or "cats" for brevity. In one variety, the heavy fractions are vaporized in a heating unit, and passed through a vessel containing the granular catalyst. The temperature in the catalyst chamber is between 800° and 900° Fahrenheit; the pressures, not much above atmospheric.

The oil vapors are decomposed by the catalytic mass, depositing carbon in its pores, and the remaining carbon and hydrogen recombine to form branched-chain and cyclic hydrocarbons of lower carbon content than those in the heavy oil in the charge. As in all cracking operations, a fraction of the oil is cracked down to the lower members of the paraffin and olefin series and remains as a gas, leaving the cracking apparatus as such—the refinery gases.

The desired products, gasoline and furnace oils, are separated from the vapor stream coming from the catalytic crackers, and the heavy residues are again recycled.

The catalytic mass soon becomes blocked with carbon, and must be regenerated. The chambers carrying the mass are always in duplicate, so that when one is blocked, the vapor stream may be switched to the other. The carbon is then burned out of the first, with a diluted air—a mixture of air and combustion gases. On pure air the temperature in the mass would rise to the point of destruction of the catalyst.

A new version of the catalytic process feeds the catalyst as a fine powder into the vapor stream. As it is carried along in the stream it exerts its catalytic effect, and is then separated in a cyclone. Regeneration also takes place while it is suspended in a diluted air stream. This process is called the "fluid catalytic cracking process," though the catalyst is a solid.

The catalytic action is believed to be due to aluminum oxide in very porous condition. The catalyst as used is an acid-treated clay, or a synthetic mass of porous silica, coated with aluminum oxide. The gasoline made by this process is a superior motor fuel, and is usually blended with the much lower grades of straight-run gasolines. It is a most important product in the formulation of the aviation gasolines.

The refinery gases from the cracking units contain members of the olefine series of hydrocarbons. These are chemically very active (see page 38), and are converted into alcohols: ethyl isopropyl and isobutyl. Thus the oil industry enters the chemical field. But, of more importance, these unsaturated hydrocarbons can be polymerized into more complex hydrocarbons that are suitable for blending with gasolines to make better grade motor fuel. In this process, the propenes and the butenes from the cracking units are heated to a temperature of 400° Fahrenheit, compressed to some 200 pounds per square inch, and passed through catalytic towers. Here the catalyst is a porous mineral saturated with phosphoric acid, H_3PO_4. The product, called polymer gasoline, is a complex unsaturated compound, containing six to eight carbon atoms to the molecule. It is blended with straight-run gasolines to improve their motor fuel value.

There are two types of internal combustion engines in common use: the spark ignition, and the compression. Automobile and aircraft engines are spark ignition. The compression ignition, commonly called the Diesel engine, is used on some trucks, on fast trains, ships and stationary power plants.

In the ordinary automobile engine of the so-called four-cycle type the sequence of action in a single cylinder is:

(1) *Intake.* On a downstroke of the piston the intake valve opens, permitting a mixture of gasoline vapor and air to enter the cylinder. The mixture has been produced in the carbureter, and averages about 15 pounds of air to one pound of gasoline vapor.

(2) *Compression.* An upstroke of the piston compresses the gasoline-air mixture between the piston and the cylinder head, all valves being closed. Some engines produce a back pressure of about 100 pounds per square inch. It must not be so high as to heat the mixture to a temperature at which it might spontaneously ignite.

(3) *Ignition.* A spark jumps the gap in the spark plug and ignites the compressed mixture. The spark is so timed that ignition occurs just before the end of the compression stroke.

(4) *Expansion.* The spark heats the mixture in its immediate vicinity to ignition, and so starts a chemical reaction between the oxygen of the air and the gasoline vapor, producing carbon monoxide, CO, carbon dioxide, CO_2, and water vapor, H_2O. Heat set free in this reaction raises the temperature of the confined gases, and correspondingly the pressure, which may reach a peak of 300 to 400 pounds per square inch. This pressure pushes the piston down, creating the power to drive the car. This is the only power stroke in the two revolutions making up the four cycles, and a heavy flywheel is necessary to carry over the other strokes, which are not producers of power.

(5) *Exhaust.* On the upstroke the exhaust valve opens, and the gases of combustion are discharged through it. The cylinder is now clear for the next intake, and the exhaust valve closes and the intake valve opens at the end of the stroke.

Fuel for such an engine should be completely volatile at a relatively low temperature, and leave no residue. If it is not in vapor form in the cylinder, it will not completely burn, and any liquid residue will dilute the lubricating oil on the cylinder walls. If it is too volatile, it will evaporate wastefully in the storage tank, and in summer may form vapor in the gasoline line leading to the carbureter and interfere with, or even stop, the flow from the tank. This is called "vapor lock." Gasoline must be adapted to the temperature of the area in which it is sold. That is, in a cold area it contains more of the highly volatile constituents; in a warm region, less. The usual gasolines vaporize between 105° and 430° Fahrenheit.

The higher the pressure of compression in the cylinder the more efficiently the fuel will be converted into power—that is, the more miles per gallon. But there is a compression limit with present-day fuels. If it is exceeded the engine will "knock." We know more about preventing knock than we do of its exact cause. For any given fuel there is a critical compression pressure, and if this is exceeded knocking will occur. Some gasolines are less sensitive than others or, as is commonly said, have a better anti-knock rating. The lower members of the paraffin series, methane, ethane, and propane, have an excellent anti-knock rating; but these are gases and are impracticable for automobile fuels. The higher members of this straight-chain series become worse as the number of carbon atoms in the molecule increases. Isomers with branched chains are much better in this respect than the corresponding straight-chain hydrocarbons; the more branched the chain, the more anti-knock the product. The cyclo-paraffins are rather good fuels, and their derivatives even better. The aromatics have excellent anti-knock characteristics.

A numerical scale for indicating the anti-knocking quality of a gasoline has been devised. The standard, with a rating of 100 is trimethyl pentane,

$$CH_3-\overset{\overset{\displaystyle CH_3}{|}}{\underset{\underset{\displaystyle CH_3}{|}}{C}}-CH_2-\overset{\overset{\displaystyle }{}}{\underset{\underset{\displaystyle CH_3}{|}}{CH}}-CH_3$$

or C_8H_{18}, usually called "isooctane." While an ordinary automobile engine has a compression ratio of less than seven, this isooctane can be used without knocking in an engine with a ratio of ten. Normal heptane (a straight-chain hydrocarbon), C_7H_{16}, will knock at a compression ratio below three.

A specially designed one-cylinder engine, in which the compression ratio may be adjusted by a movable cylinder head, is used for testing fuel. The engine is run on the fuel to be tested, the compression being slowly increased until knocking is detected. Then without change in the compression adjustment the engine is run on a mixture of isooctane and heptane, the proportion of the latter being slowly increased until knocking is again detected. The percentage of isooctane in the mixture is the "octane rating" of the fuel being tested. If the mixture is 50 per cent isooctane and 50 per cent heptane, the fuel's octane rating is 50.

The straight-run gasolines usually have rather low octane numbers, those from Pennsylvania oils having numbers as low as 45. Straight-run gasolines from selected Texas crude oils may run as high as 70. Ordinary motor gasolines, in peacetime, run 72 to 74; the premium kind, 76 to 78; the third grades, sold at cut prices, as low as 60. The premium grades operate satisfactorily in engines with a compression ratio as high as 7.1; the ordinary grades at ratios of 6.5 to 6.7; the cut-price gasolines usually do not perform well at ratios above 5.7 to 6.0.

Aviation fuels for commercial use have octane numbers above 85; those for military planes, above 100. Specialties have been created with ratings as high as 200. The gasolines from the cracking stills have higher octane numbers than the straight-run distillates. Polymer gasoline runs above 85, and the product from the catalytic crackers approaches 100. Since these two are better fuels than the average automobile can effectively use, they are blended with lower-grade gasolines. The oil refiner has kept the quality of motor fuel abreast of engine design, and many of the old-model cars are getting fuels their engines cannot use to full advantage.

Certain compounds can be added to gasoline to improve the knock rating, and almost all fuels contain these agents. Ethyl alcohol, if absolutely free of water, can be mixed with gasoline; but it is expensive, and a lot is required. Light oil (see page 63) from the coke ovens is effective, but it, too, is expensive and not available in large quantity. It must be remembered that the United States consumes nearly 700,000,000 barrels of gasoline in a year, and any agent added, to be practical, must be in ample supply. The one most effective and widely used is tetraethyl lead, $Pb(C_2H_5)_4$, a liquid which is mixed with ethyl dibromide, $C_2H_4Br_2$. The mixture is sold to gasoline producers under the name of *ethyl fluid,* and is added at the refinery to motor gasolines in various proportions up to about one-tenth of a fluid ounce per gallon. Some gasolines are more sensitive to its effect than others. It will raise the octane rating 5 to 15 units.

Military aviation is pressing for ever better fuels. The aviation engine must be designed for the maximum attainable efficiency, that is, with the greatest practicable compression ratio, for weight is all-important, and fuel is not a pay load. This means fuel of the highest octane number. Civil aviation has for some time considered 85 as a minimum. Military aviation desired a fuel of 100; now there is no upper limit. The product of the cat crackers, limited in quantity, and polymer gasolines, both with generous additions of ethyl fluid, met this 100 rating. But the ethyl fluid is not a cure-all. Its effect falls off with the larger additions, and in too large amount it is likely to cause engine trouble. The problem was partly solved by a new process called *alkalation*. In the polymer process butenes are polymerized to octenes, mostly of the branched-chain variety. These octenes are then treated with hydrogen to form octanes. There is a limited amount of these olefines in the gases coming from the cracking unit. In the alkalation process butane and iso-butene can be combined to form branched-chain hydrocarbons in the presence of aluminum chloride as a catalyst. A number of seven- and eight-carbon branched-chain hydrocarbons can be built up from these refinery gases by this process, some of which have extremely high octane numbers. In similar manner, a paraffin can be linked to a benzene ring, for example, isopropyl benzene, $(CH_3)_2CHC_6H_5$, with octane rating of nearly 200. Many of these compounds are military secrets, and little may be said about them. These are the types of materials that are blended with the high-grade gasolines and ethyl fluid in the top grades of aviation fuel.

In the compression-ignition, or Diesel engines only air is drawn into the cylinder and compressed by the upstroke of the piston. The pressures reached are very high, 400 to 700 pounds per square inch, for the compressed air must be at a very high temperature. Just an instant before the end of the compression stroke, a measured quantity of a suitable fuel oil is injected into the cylinder through a spray nozzle. To secure as fine atomization as possible, this oil reaches the nozzle at pressure as high as 20,000 pounds per square inch. The hot compressed air ignites the oil. The burning of the oil generates heat which further raises the pressure in the cylinder and pushes the piston down, thus producing power. At the end of the downstroke, the exhaust valve opens and the gases of combustion are discharged, usually with the help of a blast of fresh air furnished by an air pump. This leaves the cylinder charged with air for the following compression stroke.

A high-octane fuel is not necessary for the Diesel engine. Diesel fuels are rated on cetane ($C_{16}H_{34}$) numbers and have much higher boiling temperatures than those that must be vaporized through a carbureter. They range through kerosenes into heavy fuel oils.

The straight-run gasolines require further refining before they are marketed; those from the cracking stills, much less. The straight-run gasolines often contain some light olefines which, on storage, polymerize slowly into gums that block fuel lines and the fine jets in carbureters. To remove these unsaturated compounds strong sulphuric acid is added to the gasoline. Strong agitation is required to mix the heavy acid with the light oil. The unsaturated compounds combine with the sulphuric acid to form sulphonates, and settle out as sludge when the agitators stop. The gasoline is then washed with water to remove most of the remaining acid. A "doctor solution" (made by dissolving lead oxide in caustic soda solution) is thoroughly mixed with the gasoline to remove sulphur compounds, which will oxidize in an automobile engine to form sulphuric acid and corrode the engine and exhaust lines. The sulphides of lead formed settle out, and the gasoline is given a final water wash and again distilled to insure the proper boiling range. The ethyl fluid and dyes to indicate the presence of the lead are finally added, and the product is ready for storage and market.

The premium gasoline usually has added to it an inhibitor to prevent gum formation. Inhibitors are organic reducing agents which absorb oxygen—this latter seems to be responsible for much of the gum formation. Phenols, amines, and quinones are the basis of most of the inhibitors, one of the best being para-amino-phenol, $NH_2C_6H_4OH$.

The residual oils left after gasoline extraction are converted into fuel oils and lubricants. The fuel oils may be recovered in any of the various grades from the separating column of the cracking still. They go directly from the condensers to market, the lighter ones for household heating, the heavier ones for industrial use. The various grades are characterized by their boiling ranges and viscosities. Kerosene is a fraction held to a boiling range of 400° to 500° Fahrenheit. It is refined like gasoline, since a water-white product is the market standard. Because of its use in lamps, a most exacting control of the boiling limits must be exercised.

Lubricating oils are very important in this machine age. They are recovered, in a multitude of varieties, from the residues left in the straight-run gasoline stills after the gasoline and lighter fuel oils have been distilled off; that is, at temperatures not exceeding 600°. The residues are distilled for recovery of the lubricating-oil fraction. In the production of this lubricating-oil stock (called lube stock) the temperature in the still must be kept below any possibility of cracking. Live steam is injected directly in the oil in the still to permit distillation at the lowest temperature, or the operation is conducted in a vacuum apparatus.

The formulation of lubricating oils is largely an empirical matter. The heavy paraffine and asphaltum have little lubricating value, tend to crystallize out when chilled, thicken the oil at low temperatures, and must be removed. Paraffine is solidified by chilling the oil to very low temperature, and then filtered out. By the addition of special solvents asphaltum is dissolved, in a solution that will separate from the oil; liquid sulphur dioxide, furfural, and phenol are among the many such solvents. Finally, the lubricating oils are clarified by percolating through fuller's earth, or through calcined bauxite.

Modern machinery presents complex problems to the lubrication engineer. The intermittent operation of the automobile calls for a lubricating oil that does not thicken appreciably at low temperatures, for this causes hard starting in winter. This thickening is usually caused by small quantities of paraffine left behind in the refining operation. Corrective agents have been devised by the chemist to cure this difficulty. They are called *pour-point depressants*. A good example is one made of paraffine wax, and phenol or naphthol.

The high pressures created between the teeth of gears will force ordinary oil out, and metal will rub metal with disastrous results. Chemical agents have been found which are added to lubricating oil to make the so-called *high-pressure lubricants*. These are sulphur and phosphorous compounds of the hydrocarbons, both straight-chain, and aromatic. Some new phosphorous compound have been developed for the powerful aviation engines, and wil be available to the motorist after the war.

The highly refined oils prepared for the gasoline motor are also used to lubricate air compressors and general machinery Diesel lubricating oils are of higher viscosity than those for gasoline engines, and must resist higher temperatures. The cylinde oils used in reciprocating steam engines are petroleum base oil to which tallow has been added. For reciprocating marine engin lubrication, lard oil, tallow oil, or rapeseed oil is added to ver heavy mineral-oil stock.

The lubricating greases are combinations of heavy mineral oi and a soap. Sodium soaps make a fibrous grease; calcium soaps, a very smooth grease; aluminum soaps, a stringy type. The soap con tent averages between 10 and 30 per cent.

Cutting oils for use to lubricate cutting operations in moder high-speed machine shops are mixtures of light lubricating oi with a sulphonated vegetable oil (see page 124). They mix wit water to a white milky solution, which is run continuously on the cutting edge of the tool or on the surface of the grinding wheel, and act both as a cooling medium and as a lubricant. Transformer and switch oils are light petroleum oils, very carefully clarified, and absolutely free from water.

Certain countries, not well provided with natural-oil resources have attempted to make fuel and lubricating oils from coal. During World War I the Germans produced liquid fuels from naphthalene by hydrogenation at high temperatures and under pressure, using finely powdered nickel as a catalyst. The reaction, which produced the product "tetralin," is

$$\text{(naphthalene)} + 2\,\text{H}_2 = \text{(tetralin)}$$

or, in condensed form, $C_{10}H_8 + 2\,H_2 = C_{10}H_{12}$.

Though tetralin could be used in automobile engines, its boiling point is rather high for the ordinary carbureter. Being a definite chemical compound, it has a single boiling point, and not the desired wide boiling range of motor gasoline. Tetralin was satisfactory for the Diesel engine, and in the latter years of the war was the principal U-boat fuel. Another hydrogenated naphthalene, "decalin," $C_{10}H_{18}$, has properties quite similar to tetralin. Both are now used as solvents and thinners for lacquers.

But naphthalene is a by-product of the coke oven; therefore the supply is limited, and it cannot be considered as a satisfactory raw material for making the immense quantities of liquid fuels now used. A method of directly converting coal to liquid fuel is needed. Two processes have been developed, and Germany has a large number of plants in operation with an estimated capacity of some 12,000,000 tons of liquid fuel per year.

The first large-scale production was from the Bergius process, named after its inventor, though sometimes called the I.G. process, after the first corporation to undertake its development. In other countries the process is called "coal hydrogenation." It consists of the following steps:

A finely ground bituminous coal or a lignite is mixed with coal tar on a heavy oil residue. This slurry is pumped into vessels, operating at 900° Fahrenheit and 3,000 pounds per square inch pressure, and subjected to reaction with hydrogen under the same high pressure. The hydrocarbons of both the tar and the coal, and possibly a part of the carbon in the coal, take up hydrogen to form light hydrocarbons, that is, hydrocarbons with a high ratio of hydrogen to carbon in the molecule. A catalyst, usually an oxide of iron, is added to the slurry. After passing through the conversion vessel, the slurry is cooled and filtered to remove the solid catalyst. The oil is sent to distillation equipment for separation of the lighter oils, and the heavy residue is returned to the process for reuse. The tar and the volatile constituents of the coal, particularly lignite which contains up to 40 per cent volatile matter, take up most of the hydrogen; the carbon of the coal, only a little.

The oils produced are saturated compounds, for the hydrogen naturally attaches itself to any double bonds. In consequence the motor fuel fraction has an octane number below 50. To make a better motor fuel, the re-forming process of the gasoline industry is employed. This is a modified pressure cracking process and destroys some 20 per cent of the stock treated, but the recovered gasoline has an octane number above 70. Through the use of large quantities of addition agents, octane numbers as high as 85 may be obtained. This process supplied much of the aviation fuel used by Germany in the first years of the present war.

The Germans also use a second and quite different process for the production of motor fuel from coal. First, coke is produced in the usual oven, with recovery of by-products. This coke is burned in a water-gas producer to make blue gas (a mixture of carbon monoxide and hydrogen). The hydrogen in the blue gas is fortified with hydrogen to a ratio of one volume of carbon monoxide to two volumes of hydrogen. The hydrogen must be obtained by a process similar to that used in ammonia production (see page 80). This mixture is then passed through a catalyst at a temperature of 360°; pressures are quite low. The apparatus is like a boiler, the water tubes running through the catalytic mass. By carrying a steam pressure of 160 pounds per square inch, this temperature will be maintained, and at the same time steam will be produced for use in the plant. The catalyst is in the shape of small pellets, and consists of a skeleton of mineral with a coating of cobalt oxide. It becomes inactive rather quickly and must be regenerated.

The chemical reaction is an interesting one. The carbon monoxide reacts with the hydrogen to produce methyl ($-CH_3$) and methylene ($-CH_2-$) groups, which in turn, because of their free bonds, combine to form long chain hydrocarbons of the paraffin series:

$$2\ CO + 5\ H_2 = (-CH_3) + 2\ H_2O$$
$$CO + 2\ H_2 = (-CH_2-) + H_2O$$

The end product is a mixture of saturated hydrocarbons having members from C_1 to C_{50}, a large portion of which consists of paraffins from C_{20} to C_{30}. The light motor fuel fraction has a low octane number, less than 50, and must be recracked and treated with heavy additions of anti-knock compounds. The paraffins have little lubricating value and are also recracked. In consequence of the losses incident to the retreatments, the yields are relatively low. But the plant is neither so heavy nor so cumbersome as the I.G.-Bergius process.

Motor fuels from these processes cost three to four times that of the bulk price of gasoline at our refineries, even allowing for the lower scale of European wages. Therefore, the processes will have no economic place in our country until we have exhausted our natural petroleum resources. They are essentially war emergency developments to insure liquid fuel at any cost.

The remaining life of the known petroleum deposits has been variously estimated at from ten to fifty years. New fields are discovered from time to time, and with improved drilling equipment the deeper-lying strata may be prospected. Also more of the oil in each field is being recovered by water flooding, by repressuring of wells, by acid treatment of the oil sands. A better knowledge of the movement of oil through the sands leads to a more efficient operation of the wells. The steady improvement of refineries increases the yields of products most in demand. The polymer process is recovering oil from the refinery gases, that formerly were wasted or burned under the stills. The automotive engine designer can help to conserve fuel by perfecting more efficient engines. There are vast resources of oil-bearing shales which some day will be made to furnish a large amount of liquid fuel. The future of our oil supply is not wholly discouraging.

From time to time the so-called "colloidal fuel" is spoken of as a substitute for petroleum fuels. It is a mixture of 40 per cent pulverized coal and 60 per cent fuel oil. The coal must be ground extremely fine, much finer than for direct burning as pulverized coal; and even then it is difficult to keep it suspended in the oil. Any coal that settles out blocks pipe lines and pumps. Such a material cannot be burned satisfactorily in an ordinary oil burner. The coal is abrasive and cuts the orifice of the burner, destroying the accurate proportioning action. Also, most oil-firing installations have no provision for handling ash, and all coals contain this foreign matter. Engineers have experimented with this fuel for twenty years without finding a satisfactory solution to the many problems that arise in its commercial application.

Chapter XII

RUBBER, NATURAL AND SYNTHETIC

There is a surprisingly large number of annual and perennial plants that produce a milky sap or latex which contains rubber. Until the war, most of our rubber supply came from tropical trees belonging to the families of Euphorbiaceae, Apocynaceae and Moreaceae. The Brazilian and the East Indian rubbers are from the genus Hevea. The Mexican shrub guayule, one of the Compositae, produces a latex in quantity. Rubber is present in the sap of the common goldenrod, milkweed, some varieties of dandelion, and in fact many common domestic plants, but it is extremely difficult to extract. The individual plants are too small to tap, and to harvest and treat whole plants for their small latex content is almost hopeless. Of the milky latex of the Hevea only 40 per cent is rubber, the rest being water and 3 per cent albuminous compounds, 3 to 4 per cent resins, and about 1 per cent mineral constituents. The latex of guayule is about 20 per cent resins and albuminoids—very difficult to separate from the rubber.

Crude rubber from such latex is not a definite chemical compound, but a mixture of quite variable composition. The varieties, in consequence, have many commercial grades and qualities depending on origin, on the method of preparation, on inherent physical properties; and there are uses for all varieties.

Latex is collected from the tree by making a V incision through the bark. A small cup is fastened at the bottom of the V. The flow of sap begins as soon as the cut is made and continues for several hours, when the cut becomes sealed by natural coagulation. Later in the day a fresh cut must be made. A tree seven or eight years old, about ten inches in diameter and forty feet high, produces

about two gallons of latex—the equivalent of five pounds of rubber—in a tapping season of seven months. Latex spoils quickly
and must be coagulated immediately into crude rubber, or else
preserved for shipping by the addition of ammonia.

The very ancient native method of preparing crude rubber is
still in use. It consists of pouring the latex slowly on a flat stick
held over a smoky fire. The latex adheres to the stick in a thin
layer, and through the action of the heat loses its water content
and coagulates. The creosotes and the pyroligneous acids in the
smoke undoubtedly cause a chemical reaction. As the operation
continues, a ball two feet in diameter is built up, layer upon
layer, somewhat sticky, not very elastic, and of a dark gray to black
color. The flat stick is withdrawn, and the ball flattened, packed
with other such balls, and shipped to market.

The modern method is to collect the latex in agitated tanks,
coagulate the rubber with a weak organic acid, such as acetic or
formic, and thoroughly wash the curd formed. This is rolled into
a sheet, baled, and sent to market. Or the latex may be preserved by
the addition of ammonia and shipped in drums or tankers, to be
subsequently precipitated at any time by the addition of acid.

Crude rubber is a mixture of a large number of polymers of
isoprene (2-methyl-1, 3-butadiene, $CH_2:CHC(CH_3):CH_2$) and has
many of the properties of a solid solution, but cannot be exactly
defined chemically. The elasticity of rubber has caused much
speculation as to the constitution of its molecule. Isoprene might
be expected to polymerize in a chainlike structure, such as,

$$\text{etc.} \quad -CH_2-\underset{\underset{CH_3}{|}}{C}:CH-CH_2-CH_2-\underset{\underset{CH_3}{|}}{C}:CH-CH_2-CH_2-\underset{\underset{CH_3}{|}}{C}:CH-CH_2-\text{etc.}$$

each simple molecule being represented by that part of the formula
between the vertical rows of dots. This alone would not explain the
remarkable elasticity. One suggestion is that the chain partakes of
the nature of a spiral, and through curling and uncurling permits
stretch and recovery. Another is that several of the isoprene molecules combine into a ring, and a number of such rings form a chain.

Stretch and recovery are due to deformation of the rings. Elastic materials are polymers of elongated molecular structure and with very little of the cross-linkage between parallel chains that is characteristic of the hard, brittle resins. The contrast in molecular weight between the rubber molecule (several hundred thousand) and isoprene (only 68) shows the great complexity of the rubber molecule.

About thirty years ago chemists attempted to produce a synthetic rubber from isoprene, and also from a closely related compound, dimethyl butadiene, C_6H_{10}; but in both cases the results were quite unsatisfactory. The writer rode on tires made from dimethyl butadiene in 1914, and they lacked much of the quality of natural rubber tires, poor as these were.

The processing of crude rubber in the manufacturing plant varies greatly according to the ultimate use. The smoked varieties of the crude balls must be disintegrated and washed to remove bark, leaves, and other foreign matter. The plantation sheeted rubbers do not require this washing, since it was done in the field preparation.

It is necessary to dry the washed rubber, for any remaining moisture would cause blisters in the subsequent processing. This can be done slowly in open air, or rapidly in vacuum dryers. The dried rubber is then broken down in a mill: a heavy, powerful machine, consisting of a pair of smooth rolls, which squeezes the mass of rubber, breaks all bubbles, and thoroughly mixes it. It is then sheeted and stored for further processing.

Almost no rubber is used in this pure state. The rubber in common articles of everyday life is compounded with a variety of materials—organic compounds, minerals, and most important of all, sulphur. Pure rubber is soft and sticky, especially when heated. Skillful compounding gives rubber widely varying properties: It can be made tough, to resist wear; elastic, to permit stretching; hard, to stand compression; gas-tight; spongy. It can be made to resist chemical reaction—but not to resist oil. It may be colored, even dyed.

Soft, tacky crude rubber combines with sulphur at elevated

temperatures, becoming harder and tougher. The softness and
elasticity of surgical rubber, and the hardness and blackness of
pipe-stem rubber, depend on the amount of sulphur added and
on the temperature and the time under heat. The treatment with
sulphur and heat is called *vulcanization.* In vulcanization, rubber
loses its tackiness and its sensitiveness to moderate changes of temperature.

It is the receptivity of rubber to the formation of the soft rubber mix, to the shaping and curing of this with loss of plasticity
but retention of the desired degree of elasticity, that makes it so
valuable. Space is lacking here to describe all the various mixtures
of rubber for a thousand uses; but the general principles can be
easily understood.

Carbon black, next in importance to sulphur in forming the
rubber mix, is made by decomposing a hydrocarbon, such as
methane or ethane. Heat alone will break up these gases into
carbon and hydrogen, the carbon being in a very finely divided
condition. An older, though even more important method of de
composing the gas is to burn it in a series of small jets, impinging
the flame on a cold piece of steel. Soot forms on the cold steel
and may be scraped off and collected. The very tough treads of
automobile tires owe their resistance to wear to carbon black in
corporated in the rubber.

Zinc oxide is also an important ingredient of vulcanized rubber. The combination of rubber, sulphur, carbon black, and zinc
oxide seems to be chemical in nature, though many attempts have
been made to explain the remarkable properties imparted to the
rubber by these materials as physical in character.

To cheapen the rubber mix, various mineral fillers are used
such as magnesium oxide, finely divided calcium carbonate, even
white clay. White rubber cannot contain carbon black, and the
additions are here limited to the white materials, such as zinc oxide
magnesium oxide, calcium carbonate, and clays; it is never as tough
as rubber containing carbon. Colored rubbers use carbon, if at
all, only in very small amount. The coloring agents used are oxide
of iron for brown, antimony sulphide for dark red, ultramarine

for blue, zinc chromate for yellow. Dyes and lake colors give the brilliant hues to the bathing accessories.

Many organic compounds are used in the rubber industry. Pine tar, stearic acid, derivatives of vegetable oils, and glue are used to soften the batch and assist in breaking it down in the rubber mill. Vulcanization may be hastened at lower temperatures by adding "accelerators," some of which are so active they cause combination of the sulphur at very low temperatures. These are organic amides, some of great complexity. Two of the most important are thiocarbanilide, $(C_6H_5NH)_2CS$, and diphenylguanidine, $(C_6H_5NH)_2C:NH$.

Rubber "ages," that is, deteriorates, when exposed to air and sunlight. It is now customary to prevent this by adding antioxidants to the rubber mix. Phenyl beta-naphthylamine, $C_6H_5 NH C_{10}H_7$, is an excellent antiaging reagent and is found in most of the better grades of tires.

The rubber stock for a red inner tube is compounded from: smoked sheet rubber, 100 pounds; calcium carbonate, 15; zinc oxide, 5; stearic acid, $2\frac{1}{4}$; sulphur, 2; iron oxide, $1\frac{1}{2}$; antioxidant, 1; accelerator, $\frac{3}{4}$. This contains no carbon black, since the wearing properties and toughness which would require carbon are unnecessary, and the red color is wanted. A black tube would use a small amount of carbon and omit the oxide of iron.

A tough-tread stock consists of the following: smoked sheet rubber, 100 pounds; carbon black, 49; zinc oxide, 5; stearic acid, 3; pine tar, 2; sulphur, 3; antioxidant, 1; accelerator, 1.

These materials are incorporated on heavy rolls. Each ingredient is carefully weighed, put into a marked container, and delivered to the operator. The rubber is thrown on the rolls and milled until well spread out, and the rest of the ingredients are added gradually as they are incorporated. The rubber sticks to the front roll and, as it revolves, is cut with a knife and thrown back into the feed space. Since one roll runs at a slightly higher speed than the other, the mixing is a sort of kneading operation. The milling generates a great deal of heat, and the temperature must not be permitted to rise to the point of vulcanization.

When the batch has been thoroughly milled and all the ingredients are completely and uniformly incorporated, the rubber is ready for molding. It is pressed into the forms, and is heated under pressure to the vulcanizing temperature.

A tire casing is made up of several parts. Each of these is prepared as a unit, and then the whole is assembled. First the steel wires ("beads") are placed on a form; next the rubber-impregnated fabric is laid on in layers, the edges wrapped around the bead. The side walls are of a rubber compounded for flexibility; the tread is a stock designed for toughness. The several layers are flat cylinders as assembled, and in no way resemble the finished tire. This soft ill-shaped ring is then placed in the vulcanizer—a heavy cast-iron mold the exact shape and size of the finished tire. The mold is opened and closed by hydraulic cylinders, and is hollow and connected to a steam line. The ring of rubber is set in the mold with a rubber tube inside, connected to a source of compressed air. The mold is closed, and air let into the tube, which expands and forces the soft rubber ring, the future tire, into the curve of the mold. This shapes the tire and impresses the tread design, the brand and other markings. Then steam is turned into the mold, vulcanizing the whole. The modern vulcanizing machine is almost automatic. The operator merely inserts the built-up casing, starts the machine, and takes out the finished tire.

The several grades of tires vary in quality according to the proportions of fabric and new rubber they contain. *Reclaimed rubber* is used in nearly all tires to facilitate compounding. The cheaper tires contain more in proportion, particularly when the price of crude rubber is high. There are many grades of "reclaim," as it is called, the source largely determining the quality. The highest grades are made from soft rubber—inner tubes, for example.

In reclaiming rubber from tires, the steel beads are cut off in a special machine. The carcass is then shredded in a cutter. The chips are charged into an autoclave, or pressure cooker, and heated in a weak caustic soda solution to about 350° Fahrenheit for twelve to twenty-four hours. This disintegrates the cotton fabric and dis-

COATING FABRIC WITH RUBBER
Compounding mill in background

SYNTHETIC RUBBER

Coagulating the latex; ameripol

solves out some of the sulphur and fillers. The rubber is then thoroughly washed and sent to rolls for milling into sheets.

Reclaimed rubber is soft and helps in the milling of crude rubber, so that it is largely used in compounding. Footwear, rubber heels, the cheaper grades of hot-water bottles, and many varieties of mechanical rubber goods contain goodly proportions. It is much inferior to new crude rubber, lacking the elasticity and toughness of the virgin product.

As in the case of many natural products of the vegetable class, the climatic conditions surrounding the growth of rubber greatly influence the quality of the product; this does not have the uniformity desired. Uniformity is necessary in modern assembly-line production. Natural rubber varies greatly in price over the years. Chemists have long sought to synthesize rubber, but its molecule is a complicated structure. The nitrogenous constituents (albuminoids) and the resins of the natural product undoubtedly have a most important influence on quality. All the early attempts at making a true synthetic product have resulted in failure.

The so-called "synthetic rubbers" are chemically unlike the natural product. They are organic materials with many of the properties usually associated with rubber. They are highly polymerized compounds, of many different origins, which have elasticity and flexibility; and some of them vulcanize to tough rubberlike masses. Some synthetic rubber may excel natural rubber for certain purposes, but no one gives anything like the all-around service obtainable from natural rubber. For example, some are more resistant to oil than natural rubber, some will outwear the natural product, but none of them combines the wear, toughness, and performance under wide ranges of temperatures that is obtained from natural rubber.

The *isoprene* rubber of 1910 and the *methyl* rubber of 1912 are of historical interest alone. A few rather unsatisfactory tires and some battery cases for German submarines seem to have been the extent of their use.

Neoprene is an American development and has been in production here for many years. It vulcanizes, but with insufficient tough-

ness for a good tire compound. It has excellent resistance to decomposition by oils and is used for the lining of hose to convey
oil, for gaskets, electrical insulation, and for many chemical purposes. It deteriorates with age more quickly than some of the
newer products.

Neoprene is made from acetylene and hydrochloric acid. The
acetylene is bubbled through a solution of cuprous chloride, CuCl,
which acts as a catalyst to condense the acetylene to vinyl-acetylene:

$$2 \, C_2H_2 = HC\!:\!C\!-\!CH\!:\!CH_2$$

Hydrochloric acid converts this to chloroprene:

$$HC\!:\!C\!-\!CH\!:\!CH_2 + HCl = H_2C\!:\!CCl\!-\!CH\!:\!CH_2$$

When chloroprene is heated with a catalyst an internal rearrangement of the molecule takes place, and neoprene is formed, and
which may be polymerized to molecular weight above 100,000. The
probable formula of the polymer is $(-H_2C\!-\!CCl\!:\!CH\!-\!CH_2\!-)_n$.
Stopping the polymerization at exactly the desired point is a real
problem that is not completely solved. In consequence neoprene,
like most of these rubber substitutes, shows material variation in
the successive batches. Blends of many such must be made for
commercial applications. The production of neoprene requires care
in the choice of raw materials, in their extreme purification, and
in processing, and in consequence it is not cheap as compared to
natural rubber.

Koroseal is a soft rubbery material used for electrical insulation,
mechanical goods, rubber sheeting, and coated fabrics. It may be
produced in transparent sheets and is used for raincoats and um-
brella coverings, often in brilliant shades. It is not vulcanizable.

Koroseal is made from ethylene dichloride, $CH_2Cl\!:\!CH_2Cl$, this
being made from ethylene gas and chlorine. The dichloride reacts with caustic soda to form vinyl-chloride:

$$CH_2Cl\!:\!CH_2Cl + NaOH = CH_2\!:\!CHCl + NaCl + H_2O$$

The vinyl-chloride is then polymerized to a rubberlike material
which has the formula $(-CH_2\!-\!CHCl\!-)_n$. It is milled like rubber
with various plasticizers and softening agents to make it flexible.

Thiokols, or polysulphide rubbers, are made from ethylene
dichloride and sodium polysulphide. There are many varieties,

and they are probably not definite chemical compounds, but rather a mixture of several which approximates the general formula

$$(—CHS—\overset{\displaystyle \underset{\|}{S}}{\underset{\displaystyle \underset{\|}{S}}{CHS}}—)_n$$

The thiokols have extraordinary resistance to oil and to chemical reaction, and they are widely used for lining hose, tanks, even reservoirs designed for the storage of aviation gasoline. They have a rather unpleasant odor. The thiokols cannot be vulcanized to tough-wearing structure and have no place in tire manufacture, though extensive experiments were made to fit them for the production of retreads.

Buna S, or styrene rubber, is a German development since the First World War. This product can be vulcanized to a tough-wearing tread material. It has very little tear resistance, so that a surface cut tends to continue to open up. In road service the Buna S tires heat up more than natural rubber—even to the point of deterioration of the tire fabric. Buna S is much more sensitive to temperature changes than vulcanized natural rubber, and should be specifically formulated for hot and for cold climates. Fortunately it blends with natural rubber, and in a 50 per cent admixture these disadvantages are to a great part corrected. Even 25 per cent of natural rubber and 75 per cent Buna S makes a tire that is fairly satisfactory, though in no sense equal to the better grades of natural rubber tires.

Buna S is made by the simultaneous polymerization of butadiene, $CH_2:CH—CH:CH_2$, and styrene, $C_6H_5CH:CH_2$, in the presence of a soap catalyst, and under carefully controlled temperatures and pressures.

Styrene is found in small amounts in the light oil from the coke oven, and in the gases from the petroleum cracking still. But the quantities available from these sources cannot supply any large-scale rubber program. Styrene may be produced synthetically by heating benzene and ethylene vapors together, forming ethyl benzene. Aluminum chloride is used as a catalyst. The ethyl benzene is then dehydrogenated to styrene. The reactions are:

$$C_6H_6 + H_2C:CH_2 = C_6H_5CH_2CH_3$$
$$C_6H_5CH_2CH_3 = C_6H_5CH:CH_2 + H_2$$

The dehydrogenation takes place at low red heat.

The yields are not high, for many side reactions enter into this type of chemical operation. Benzene is not too plentiful, for it is required for explosives and many other essential needs. Fortunately benzene can be made from petroleum, and several cracking plants will be available for the transformation of petroleum oils into toluene and benzene. Styrene may also be made from acetylene, but that is in even more critical demand than benzene, and is much more expensive.

Butadiene is a gas at ordinary temperatures, but can be liquefied by moderate pressure; it must be stored in pressure containers. It may be made from ethyl alcohol, C_2H_5OH, which is derived either from petroleum or from the fermentation of molasses or grain. Petroleum offers by far the cheapest source of this alcohol. Ethyl alcohol may be cracked directly into butadiene, by passing the alcohol vapor through a heated catalyst:

$$2\ C_2H_5OH = CH_2:CH—CH:CH_2 + H_2O + 2\ H_2$$

This conversion is very wasteful of the raw material, the actual recovery being only about 25 per cent of the theoretical (that is, one gallon of alcohol will only produce one pound of butadiene). Moreover the cracking produces other products that contaminate the butadiene, some of which are very difficult to remove.

A better method of converting ethyl alcohol into butadiene is to make acetaldehyde first, by oxidation with air in the presence of a catalyst:

$$2\ C_2H_5OH + O_2 = 2\ CH_3CHO + 2\ H_2O$$

Two molecules of the aldehyde may be condensed to aldol in a weak acid solution:

$$2\ CH_3CHO = CH_3CHOHCH_2CHO$$

Hydrogen is added to the aldol to form butylene glycol:

$$CH_3CHOHCH_2CHO + H_2 = CH_3CHOHCH_2CH_2OH$$

The glycol, in the form of vapor, is passed through a heated catalyst of aluminum oxide to form butadiene:

$$CH_3CHOHCH_2CH_2OH = CH_2:CH—CH:CH_2 + 2\ H_2O$$

This operation is not too complicated for commercial use, since it may be carried out in a series of continuous processes, and the efficiencies are quite good. A little more than two pounds of excellent quality product may be made from a gallon of alcohol. In Germany, where petroleum is scarce and there are no surplus crops for the production of fermentation alcohol, the starting raw material is calcium carbide. Acetylene is produced from this, and oxidized to acetaldehyde by bubbling it through a dilute sulphuric acid containing mercury sulphate as a catalyst. Eight tons of calcium carbide will give one ton of Buna S.

Butadiene may also be made by cracking a mixture of steam and cyclohexane at 1300° Fahrenheit. The cyclohexane is made by hydrogenation of benzol. A gallon of benzol will give about two pounds of butadiene.

The waste gas from the petroleum cracking stills contains small amounts of butadiene, but in a most complex admixture from which recovery is difficult. With specially designed cracking equipment, however, using as raw material light petroleum oils containing from four to six carbon atoms, it is possible to obtain butadiene in such concentration as to make commercial extraction possible. The petroleum industry is skilled in the design and operation of large cracking units that could meet the large demands synthetic rubber might require, so that this is a logical source of raw material.

The production of butadiene from petroleum by cracking starts with butane and pentane—that is, medium low paraffins. These are broken down to olefins, principally normal, and isobutenes, in a cracking operation at high temperature and under high pressure. The butenes are then catalytically cracked to split off more hydrogen, forming butadiene. Efficiency is not so high as might be desired, but the raw materials—waste gases from ordinary refineries—are plentiful. By-products of butadiene production find a place in the production of alkalate gasoline, which is a valuable constituent of aviation fuels. Distillation of butadiene obtained in this manner does not yield a sufficiently pure product; it is purified in a complicated way by the use of selective solvents.

The copolymerization of the butadiene and the styrene takes place in a soap solution, in a pressure vessel. A peroxide is used as a catalyst. The kettle is charged with the soap solution and the liquid butadiene (under pressure) and the styrene are pumped in—three parts butadiene to one part styrene. The catalyst is added last. After a slight warming, which starts the reaction, the container must be cooled to a very closely controlled temperature and held there. The mass is then agitated for hours, even days, until the desired molecular aggregation is attained. By the use of more catalyst, the reaction can be greatly speeded up; but if this is too rapid it may bring overpolymerization.

The result of the reaction is a synthetic latex, insoluble in the soap solution, and much dispersed. The latex is coagulated by adding a weak acid which throws it down as a curd. This is separated from the soap solution by screening. The curd is carefully washed to remove the adhering soap solution, pressed into cakes, and milled in rubber rolls to a sheet. The reaction might be written:

$$n\ CH_2CHCH:CH_2 + n\ C_6H_5CH:CH_2 =$$
$$(-CH_2CH:CH(CH_2)_2CHC_6H_5-)_n$$

Buna S is quite difficult to mill, requiring much more powerful machinery than is found in a natural-rubber plant. While having a formula similar to that of rubber, it needs somewhat different carbon black and accelerators. It vulcanizes much more slowly than natural rubber. In other words it requires more and heavier machines for the same throughput.

Buna N is a copolymer of butadiene and acrylonitrile, $CH_2:CHCN$. It can be vulcanized, but the product is not tough enough for tire treads. It is very resistant to attack by oils, particularly the high-test aviation gasolines. It also ages quite well. It finds application for mechanical rubber goods, for oil hose, and for the lining of gasoline tanks.

Acrylonitrile is made from ethylene oxide and hydrocyanic acid:

$$CH_2OCH_2 + HCN = CH_2CHCN + H_2O$$

Ethylene oxide may be made by the direct oxidation of ethylene with air in the presence of a catalyst, with extraction of the product with glycol. The larger part is made from ethylene chlorhydrin by reacting this with a caustic soda solution, and distilling off the ethylene oxide:

$$CH_2ClCH_2OH + NaOH = CH_2OCH_2 + NaCl + H_2O$$

The chlorhydrin is produced by bubbling ethylene through a solution of chlorine in water:

$$C_2H_4 + Cl_2 + H_2O = CH_2ClCH_2OH + HCl$$

The hydrochloric acid is neutralized with lime, and the chlorhydrin distilled.

The Buna N process is practically the same as that for making Buna S, with the change in raw materials.

Butyl rubber is a new member of the synthetic family; there are several types. Butene, $CH_3CH_2CH:CH_2$, will polymerize by itself into a rubberlike mass; but this has little utility. Isobutene, $(CH_3)_2C:CH_2$, does likewise. If the two butenes, with butadiene and a little isoprene, are polymerized together, a rubbery mass is produced which can be vulcanized. Tires have been made of this rubber, but there is much difference of opinion as to their serviceability. The polymerization takes place at low pressures and temperatures, and requires simpler apparatus than that of the Buna rubbers. The simple raw materials and equipment required make butyl much the cheapest of the synthetic rubbers, and with further development it may become of great commercial importance. The Bunas are not suitable for the manufacture of inner tubes, whereas the butyls seem to have immediate possibility for this.

The problems of milling and vulcanization of these synthetic products are only temporary. It took twenty years to produce a tire of natural rubber that would consistently give twenty-five thousand miles of road service, and such performance cannot be expected immediately from entirely new chemical products. Once the synthetic materials are available in quantity, the problems of manufacture will soon be solved, with a wholly new tire engineering and design.

The synthetic products are not synthetic rubber; they are in no sense chemical duplicates of the natural rubber. Many of the unfavorable performance records were due to their having been manipulated as though they were the same. Once this was understood, and new procedures developed, much better road service resulted. The synthetics are stiffer than natural rubber; they develop much more internal heat on flexure; they are more sensitive to changes of temperature. Admixture of natural rubber reduces their shortcomings to considerable degree. Perhaps some day a third copolymer will be introduced to overcome all their unfavorable characteristics. These problems of technology are not insoluble.

Tires, important as they are to our economy, are by no means the only use for rubber. The synthetics can well replace it for many other purposes: electrical insulation, impregnated fabrics, gaskets and mechanical goods, elastic threads, and the like. Where oil is present, natural rubber is of little use, and here the synthetics are preeminent.

There is a whole series of rubberlike products made from vegetable oils and ethylene glycol. They have very little mechanical strength and cannot be vulcanized. Reinforced with fabric, they will find many applications. There are several vinyl compounds (see page 105) that, when backed up with a textile, take the place of rubber in electrical insulation, hospital sheeting and sanitary goods, and waterproofing. In many cases the substitutes serve better than the natural rubber, and here there is little doubt that they have already established themselves.

Chapter XIII

RESINS AND PLASTICS

Resins are amorphous organic compounds of vegetable origin. They have very high molecular weights—which indicates that the molecules are large and of polymer character. Instead of melting sharply at some definite point like true chemical compounds, they remain soft without becoming liquid through a wide range of temperature. When softened by heat they may be pressed or molded into any shape. Any resins which actually melt may be cast into forms. Certain ones may be dissolved in suitable solvents and used in solution as base material for enamels and lacquers. Another group, of which common shellac is an example, may be ground to powder and mixed with filler. The mixture when heated becomes soft and may be molded in a press—for example, into the common phonograph record.

Materials of similar appearance and properties may be made synthetically. These are called *resinoids;* but, now that they have become so very common, there is a popular tendency to call them resins.

Such natural and synthetic resinous products as—either alone or mixed with filler—soften when heated so that they may be pressed into molds, after which they again harden, are called *plastics.* Their utilitarian value results from their physical properties rather than from their specific chemical composition, though naturally the latter governs the former. In composition they vary greatly; hence, chemical classification is not simple. They may, however, be divided into groups, the individual members of which will show some chemical relationship.

The two main groups of synthetic plastics are:

(1) *Thermoplastic* resins. These soften when heated, and can be rolled into sheets, extruded through dies into rods, tubes, and other lineal shapes, or pressed into a mold or die. After they cool they are rigid. They may be repeatedly heated for molding purposes.

(2) *Thermosetting* resins. These soften to a degree when heated and, in this plastic condition, may be pressed into molds; but if the heating is continued they set firm and hard, and will not again soften, even at higher temperatures. A chemical reaction has taken place during the molding, and the new product is not a plastic.

These groupings apply whether the resinous constituent is the sole component or, as in most commercial products, is mixed with an inert substance or filler, such as fiber, wood flour, or even mineral.

An example of a natural thermoplastic is asphaltum, which is used in the common molded storage battery case. This is a hydrocarbon found in petroleum, or in a lake in the island of Trinidad. Shellac, mentioned above, is exuded by an insect, *Laccifer lacca,* and is an aromatic compound belonging to the thermoplastic group. To the natural products, the chemist has added a long list of synthetics of the thermoplastic types. There are no natural thermosetting resins.

The oldest synthetic plastic is *Celluloid.* This trade name is given to a product composed largely of nitrocellulose, of which a more accurate name is cellulose nitrate; competitive products similar in composition to Celluloid, are Fiberloid, Pyralin, Viscoloid, and Xylonite. It was invented about seventy-five years ago in the United States, and in spite of certain drawbacks and severe competition from more modern discoveries it continues to be manufactured to the extent of some 8,000 to 10,000 tons per year. The principal use today is for photographic film, though toys, toilet articles, and heavy transparent sheets also are important. Celluloid belongs to the thermoplastic group.

Its manufacture involves the preparation of a suitable grade of cellulose nitrate containing about 11 per cent nitrogen (which is about 1.5 per cent less than that in the kind used for making smokeless powder). The nitrate for Celluloid must be soluble in certain preferred solvents. This is more important than an exact chemical composition, and in consequence the soluble nitrate is not a definite chemical compound but rather a mixture of several compounds, carrying from two to six nitrate groups attached to the cellulose. The process of preparation is largely empirical—one determined by experience.

The cellulose used for nitration is made from short-fiber cotton, cotton linters, or wood pulp. Whatever the material, it must be carefully purified by long boiling with dilute caustic soda solution, and then energetic bleaching with chlorine. All foreign matter must be removed. The pure cellulose fiber is then carefully dried in an open fluffy condition.

For nitration a mixture of nitric and sulphuric acids, diluted to a specified strength and cooled to a low temperature, is prepared in advance. The nitration apparatus is a pot of stainless steel provided with a very effective stirring apparatus. This is charged with a weighed quantity of the mixed acid, and checked for temperature. A weighed batch of the dried cotton is stirred in the acid. The nitrating operation lasts about thirty minutes. All weights, acid strengths, temperatures, and time must be carefully checked, for reactions in the treatment of organic compounds with nitric acid are hazardous, with the possibility of fire, even explosion.

The chemical reaction of the nitration cannot be exactly written because of the somewhat indefinite character of the product, consisting of several nitrates, but it closely approximates:

$$C_6H_{10}O_5 + 3\ HNO_3 = C_6H_7O_2(NO_3)_3 + 3\ H_2O$$

The water produced in the reaction would stop the nitration, were sulphuric acid not present to take it up as fast as it is formed. The sulphuric acid plays no other part.

At the completion of the nitration, the mass of pulp and spent acid is dropped into a whirling centrifuge, which whizzes the liquid out of the fiber. This looks like the original cotton linters, but feels somewhat harsher. The spent acid is fortified with fresh strong acids and used again, but finally picks up so much water and becomes so extended that it must be sent to a recovery plant, or disposed of in other operations.

The nitrocellulose is subjected to elaborate and thorough washing to remove every last trace of acid, for any that is left in the product will cause yellowing, and sometimes dangerous decomposition. Finally all the water is displaced with alcohol. Saturated with alcohol, nitrocellulose can be safely transported and stored.

For conversion to Celluloid the fibrous nitrocellulose, still saturated with alcohol, is thrown into a kneading machine; camphor is added, and the mass is made into a dough. If the final Celluloid is to be colored, dyes are added to the mixer. This dough is then sent to the extruding machines for pressing into rods and tubes, or to rolls for forming sheets. These sheets are then piled, and the piles pressed into blocks. The sheet Celluloid found on the market is sliced from such blocks and polished or otherwise surface-finished.

Celluloid can be pressed into rather simple molds that have been slightly warmed. Pieces of celluloid can be joined with a cement made from a nitrocellulose solution. It is so inflammable that manipulation must be slight, and at a low temperature.

The raw materials for photographic film are most carefully selected, and the processing, particularly the washing, is very exact. In the kneading, camphor and softening and plasticizing agents are added—usually esters of the higher alcohols, such as tricresyl phosphate, $(CH_3C_6H_4)_3PO_4$. The resulting mass is dissolved in a volatile solvent to a thick viscous solution, and spread evenly over the surface of a highly polished revolving drum. The base material sets as the solvent evaporates, and is stripped off as a sheet. This must be aged to remove the last traces of solvent; it is then cut to size. The film is five one-thousandths of an inch in thickness. The sensitized coating, a mixture of gelatine and silver halides, is applied in a separate operation.

Another cellulose ester, the *acetate* used in synthetic yarns (see page 103), is also widely used as a plastic. By itself, it is rather brittle; but it can be plasticized with phthalates and organic phosphates. This plastic has many commercial names—Tenite, Lumarith, Plastacele, etc. For molding it is usually mixed with various fillers—wood flour, paper pulp, even mineral powders. It, too, is a thermoplastic. It can be produced in sheet form in the same manner as nitrocellulose, and is the base of the "safety film" used for home movies. It ignites less easily and burns more slowly than Celluloid film.

A wholly new group of cellulose compounds has recently entered this field. They are *cellulose ethers,* in which the chemical groups, methoxy, —OCH_3, and ethoxy, —OC_2H_5, are joined to the cellulose molecule in varying proportions. They are principally used for coatings and substitutes for textile products, but have been extruded into pipe and tubing. In combination with other plastic materials, they serve as softening agents.

Another of the older plastics has a *casein* base. Its trade names are Galalith and Ameroid. Casein is a complex amino compound comprising about 3 per cent of skimmed milk. It is precipitated as a curd by the addition of a small amount of a dilute mineral acid, and is skimmed from the whey. This curd is mixed with dyes and filling materials in a kneading machine, and is extruded in the form of rods and tubes. It cannot be pressure-molded into intricate shapes. The rods and tubes are immersed in a weak formaldehyde solution which sets the casein to a hornlike and tough structure. The finished articles, usually jewelry and ornaments for trimmings, are machined from the rod and tube stock.

The seeds of the soybean and many other legumes are rich in vegetable proteins, sometimes called "vegetable casein." The beans are·crushed, and the oil first extracted by pressing or by solvent extraction. The oil-free bean cake is then treated with sodium hydroxide to dissolve the casein. This can be separated by precipitating with acid. Vegetable casein is not considered as equal to casein from milk, but it is slowly finding its place in the plastic industry, principally in mixtures with other plastic materials. Because of the enormous potential supplies of vegetable casein, extensive work is in progress to better evaluate it.

Casein plastics are difficult to mold, and their low water resistance causes them to check and warp in an atmosphere of changing humidity. Admixture with some of the more water-resistant plastics improve their stability. It is some sort of mixture of this kind that has been considered as construction material for the future automobile body.

The outstanding advantage of these thermoplastic materials lies in the ease of molding to exact dimensions, a quick mechanical operation producing a finished article. The molding compound is composed of a resinoid and a filling material, in proportions depending on the mechanical properties desired in the finished article. The components are ground together in a mill, or incorporated on rolls similar to those used in compounding rubber. The mixture, in the form either of powder or of tablets, is shipped to the molding plant in bulk containers.

There are two systems of molding: injection and intermittent. Thermoplastics are molded by injection; the intermittent system is suited to either of the two classes of plastics.

In the injection system, the molding powder is charged into a hopper on the machine, from which it is fed in measured batches to an intermediate heating chamber. Here it is softened to the desired degree, and is then forced by the ram of the press into the mold. As soon as the mold is filled, it is cooled by circulating water through channels within it, after which the press may be opened, discharging the product. The whole operation is automatic. The mold is in two parts to facilitate extraction of the formed pieces.

Thermosetting resins cannot be heated in this way before entering the mold, and must be formed by an intermittent system.

In the intermittent system, the die is also in two parts; one part is clamped to the bed of the press, the other to the movable head. The powdered plastic is measured out in a cup of suitable size so that just the right quantity is supplied to each cavity: too little would tend to give improper density or even an imperfect part; too much would strain the die or might even break the press. For small parts it is customary to tablet just the right amount in a special machine; this speeds up the production of the heavy presses. The press is opened, and the plastic charged into the lower half of the mold. The press is closed, and steam turned into the hollow dies. The plastic softens and is forced into all corners of the mold. This heating is continued until the plastic sets. After reaching the desired temperature, the press is opened and the molded part removed while still hot.

The pressures for molding run from ten to twenty tons per square inch, and large objects, such as radio cabinets, require very heavy hydraulic equipment. The molding cycle varies between one and ten minutes, depending in part on the kind of plastic, and in part on the thickness of the section of the part to be molded.

Small objects, such as bottle caps, are made in multiple-cavity dies, often as many as fifty at a time. In such production, a box with holes which register with the cavities is slipped on the bottom half of the die, this dropping tablets into all cavities at the same time. A special composition of molding powder is used, which permits snapping the caps off the screw threads and avoids the time-consuming operation of turning each.

Metal inserts can be set in the die, and the plastic firmly embeds them. The plastic must have the same thermal expansion as the metal insert; otherwise changes of temperature will cause this to loosen. Molds for intricate shapes containing holes are so made that the pins which form the holes can be withdrawn for removal of the finished part.

From the chemical point of view there are two kinds of thermo-setting resins: *phenolic* and *amino* resins. The phenolics—Bakelite, Durez, Fiberlon, Textolite—are made from phenol and formaldehyde. Cresols and xylenols may be substituted for part of the phenol, and most resins in this group contain mixtures of these very similar coal-tar derivatives. Other aldehydes as well as formaldehyde may be used; but this is so cheap and so plentiful that it is the one most used. Because such substitutions are possible, resinoid formation is a class reaction rather than a specific one.

The phenol, for example, is heated with formaldehyde, the commercial product being a 40 per cent solution in water. This water, together with that formed by reaction, is boiled off at a low temperature. A partially reacted product resembling molten glass forms in the kettle; this is run out and cast into molds and cooled to a solid. This is ground fine and mixed with the chosen filler (most commonly ground wood or wood flour), and with a condensation reagent (hexamethylene tetramine, $C_6H_{12}N_4$). So long as the resinoid is acid in reaction, it may be heated without change. In alkaline media, it polymerizes rapidly, particularly at elevated temperatures. Hexamethylene tetramine is neutral, but when heated gives off ammonia and becomes alkaline. The phenolic resinoid, containing hexamethylene tetramine, is stable as long as it is not heated above the decomposition temperature of the condensing reagent; once that temperature is exceeded, it will polymerize to a hard, infusible product. The molding powder (described on page 164) is charged into the molding press, steam is turned into the dies, and the resinoid softens. The high pressure drives the softened product into all parts of the cavity. As heating is continued, the hexamethylene tetramine decomposes, the mass becomes alkaline, and polymerization takes place. The result is a set object.

The chemical reactions involved are so complex that it is not possible to write them in equation form. The phenol, C_6H_5OH, combines with formaldehyde, HCHO, to form a phenylmethalol, $HOC_6H_4CH_2OH$, in the reaction kettle. In the hot mold this decomposes, losing water, to form $—C_6H_3OHCH_2—$; that is, the hydroxyl of the methalol group has acquired one of the hydrogen atoms from the benzene ring forming water, which is driven off in the hot press. This leaves two free bonds, ready to combine with groups containing similar free bonds, into polymers of high molecular weight— that is, into the set resinoid. Unlike the synthetic rubbers, these resinoids do not tend to form long straight-chain polymers, and there is much cross linkage; therefore they are not elastic.

By altering the proportions of phenols and formaldehyde, the phenolics can be made quite fluid when heated; and in the melted form they can be cast into molds. Cast phenolics usually do not contain fillers. They can be colored by adding dyes. To insure final setting, an accelerator is added, facilitating polymerization at low temperatures. The molds are of type metal, and are used but once. The setting takes place in the mold, and is carried out in an oven. Casting is chiefly into rods and tubes, from which are machined various objects—mechanical parts, beads, bracelets, pipe stems, etc.

The annual tonnage of these phenolic molding compounds is

enormous, greatly exceeding that of any other thermosetting plastic. They find application in the production of a long line of electrical equipment, telephones, automobile and aviation engine distributors, bottle caps, containers, and a miscellaneous assortment of units that enter into household equipment.

Phenolic resinoids, modified in another way, are soluble in oils and form the base of varnishes and coatings. They will darken in sunlight but are very resistant to its disintegrating effect. A phenolic of this type, modified by the addition of glycerine and rosin, is widely used in varnishes as a substitute for the more expensive natural resins. It forms a particularly hard and durable finish.

The *amino* plastics—Beetle, Plaskon, Unyte—are thermosetting resinoids, characterized by brilliant colors which can be shaded off into very delicate tints. They are made from urea, $CO(NH_2)_2$, and formaldehyde, HCHO. (Both materials can be produced synthetically from abundant raw materials.) The urea is dissolved in the formaldehyde solution, the water evaporated, and the viscous colorless resinoid mixed with a highly bleached paper pulp, as a filler. The color is added during the incorporation of the filler. The amino plastics are molded like the phenolics, under pressures as high, but temperatures a bit lower.

The amino plastics do not darken with age like the phenolics, and for this reason are usually in light brilliant colors. They are widely used for buttons, ornaments, exposed electrical fixtures, radio cabinets, etc., because they can be made an exact match for any color or tint.

The chemistry of urea resin formation is:

$$CO(NH_2)_2 + HCHO = CONH_2NHCH_2OH$$

In the heated mold this breaks down to form $—NHCONHCH_2—$, which unites with similar molecules to form a very complex polymer. Melamine, $(H_2CN_2)_3$ (see page 48), also a synthetic product, can be substituted for part or most of the urea. These melamine-urea plastics have remarkable electrical properties as insulating materials, have great strength, and are used extensively for the ignition equipment of aviation engines which operate at very high temperatures.

The amino resinoids can be made oil-soluble and are widely used for enamels and lacquers, particularly those of light color. Sunlight does not darken them.

The clear water-white resins—Plexiglas and Lucite—are thermoplastics. Large quantities are used to enclose the observation and cabin openings of airplanes. They are much tougher than glass, and can be made somewhat flexible. They have a very high index of refraction (a physical property affecting the transmission of light) and are applicable to optical equipment.

They are made from acetone, $(CH_3)_2CO$, hydrocyanic acid, HCN, and methyl alcohol, CH_3OH. First, acetone cyanhydrin is produced:

$$(CH_3)_2CO + HCN = (CH_3)_2C(OH)CN$$

This is then converted to methyl methacrylate with methanol:

$$(CH_3)_2C(OH)CN + CH_3OH = CH_2{:}C(CH_3)COOCH_3 + NH_3$$

The methacrylate is then converted to $—CH_2C(CH_3)COOCH_3$, which can combine with itself repeatedly by virtue of the two unsatisfied bonds.

These plastics can be extruded into rods, tubes, and sheeted into plates of varying thickness. When heated they can be shaped, cemented, even welded into complex constructions. They are too soft for automobile glass—road dust scratches them.

Another group of resinoids of great commercial importance is formed by the Glyptals. They cannot be used for molding compounds, but do find place in paints, enamels, lacquers, and varnishes. They are remarkably resistant to weathering, being much superior to the natural resins. The modern automobile finish, which now outwears the car itself, owes its durability to these resinoids. They are made by heating glycerine, phthalic anhydride, and one or another vegetable oil to a temperature around 500° Fahrenheit. The glycerine with three hydroxyl groups and the phthalic anhydride with the equivalent of two replaceable hydrogen atoms combine to an ester; and the three-and-two combination allows polymerization of the type characterizing the resinoids. The vegetable oil is a modifying agent, and enables production of resinoids soft like balsam, hard like glass. They make possible very quick-drying varnishes, lacquers, and enamels.

Synthetic resins for adhesive purposes were mentioned in connection with the manufacture of plywood (see page 95). But they are used to cement together not only pieces of wood but paper, textiles, mineral products. The thermosetting resins are not affected by water, are resistant to many chemicals, and are not softened by heating. Signs, lampshades, and screens are made by bonding paper or textiles with these resins, and heating to the curing temperature. Cretonnes, laminated with a backing material for dressing-table tops, do not stain or soil. Substitutes for ceramic tiles can be made in similar manner.

An interesting and commercially important application of an amino resin is in the crease proofing of fabrics. A plasticizer is added to give elasticity to the very thin coating of resin, and an accelerator must be used to permit curing at very low temperatures as the treated fabric passes over a heated roll.

An amino resin is often added to the beaters in the paper industry, curing on the paper as it passes over the drying rolls, and adding greatly to its wet strength.

The plastic industry has shown remarkable development. The ability to mold an intricate part to exact dimension in a minute or two—a part which would take the machine tool hours or days to cut—is of immense value in this day of mass production. Once the die is made from hard steel, thousands of exact duplicate parts can be turned out before wear has destroyed accuracy. Then there is a wide choice among properties in the many types of plastics. The type may be selected for strength, for resistance to acid, alkali, and water, for electrical insulation, for incombustibility, for color and beauty of finish. The plastics occupy a most prominent place in our daily life, and the future holds promise of even better products, yet undiscovered.

CHAPTER XIV

EXPLOSIVES

When primitive man wanted to break a rock he had to lift it above his head and throw it against another rock. The operation was not always successful. If it was so large that he could not lift it, he built a fire against its face, or against a rock ledge; and when the rock was thoroughly heated he dashed cold water against it. Small pieces would crack off, and then he would repeat the operation.

Metal tools made it possible to drill a series of holes in rock. These were filled with water, which was allowed to freeze. The water, expanding (some 20 per cent in volume) as it changed to ice, cracked the rock. But this was possible only where winter brought freezing weather. A modification of the method described was to plug the holes tightly with soft wood, and then soak the wood with water until it swelled. Either way, a stone of predetermined dimensions would be produced, but very approximate and rough.

If a small block of stone is to be broken today, a stick or two of dynamite is laid on top of the block, covered with a pad of damp earth, and exploded. If it is a large rock, or a ledge, one or more holes are drilled and loaded with powder, which is fired. The breaking operation is instantaneous, the money cost slight, the saving in labor enormous. In some large quarries, especially those that supply broken limestone to cement plants, several hundred thousand tons of rock are blasted down at one time.

Ditches can be made by digging a line of shallow holes, charging them with powder, and exploding the charges consecutively. The ground is prepared for orchards by digging a shallow hole wherever a tree is to be, and exploding a small charge of powder in it.

The subsoil is loosened by this method, and greatly accelerated growth results. A disused chimney may be dropped on a predetermined line by a skillfully placed charge, without danger. Explosives are a most efficient chemical aid in this mechanical world.

The underlying principle of all explosions is the sudden production of a large volume of very hot gas. In a confined space, this will bring a corresponding increase in pressure, and the consequent exertion of considerable force. Explosives are designed to operate in a confined space: a gun barrel, a drill hole in a quarry, the inside of a shell. Only very large quantities of the most powerful explosives have much effect in the open air.

All explosives have two essential ingredients: oxygen and some material that will combine with it; that is to say, oxygen and something combustible, that will burn rapidly. Its union with oxygen is called *oxidation*. This is a true chemical reaction, accompanied by the generation of heat. The oxidation that occurs when oxygen of the air unites with iron to form rust is very slow, and the heat generated dissipates immediately. But when the oxidation is more rapid than the dissipation of the heat—for example, when wood burns—flame and high temperatures and all the familiar phenomena of combustion result. Everybody knows that opening the draft in a furnace will make the coal burn faster, and glow brighter, with a higher temperature. This merely means that the rate of oxidation is speeded by increasing the supply of oxygen.

Almost everybody has also had the experience of turning on the gas in the oven of a gas stove. If there is delay in lighting the burner, a small explosion occurs. If the delay is considerable, the explosion will be of considerable force. The difference between these explosions and the normal performance of the gas stove is a difference in the speed with which a given amount of gas is consumed—that is, in the speed with which a given amount of heat is produced. In the normal operation of the gas burner a very small stream of gas burns as fast as it comes in contact with air. Delayed lighting allows an accumulation of gas to mix with air and then burn all at once.

The most powerful explosives are made from raw materials such that the products of the explosion will be gases, at high temperatures and (since explosives are generally used in confined spaces) at correspondingly high pressures. For some purposes the temperatures are intentionally limited—as in gunpowders, to reduce erosion or burning of the gun barrel. The explosives used in mining coal where gas (methane) is present are designed so as not to produce temperatures that would explode the gas.

Commercial explosives are classed as "low" and "high," relatively weak and relatively powerful. The distinction is not sharp. Military explosives are divided into "propellants" and "high explosives." The commercial low explosives and the military propellants are often called powders; the high explosives have various names denoting their composition.

The explosions produced by low and high explosives differ considerably in character. The former burn rapidly—actually burn, in the sense that appreciable time is required for complete combustion. The high explosives go off with an instantaneous rearrangement of atoms, the components breaking down and simultaneously recombining into hot gases: their combustion is not progressive.

Powders are usually exploded by a flame—carried, in the firecracker, by the fuse. High explosives are *shocked* into explosion (usually by a small explosion of another explosive). Dynamite will burn quietly in the open air if lighted at one end of the stick by a flame. But if it is primed with a suitable cap, it will explode violently.

Until the latter half of the nineteenth century the only commercial or military explosive known was *black powder*. Europe first heard of it in the twelfth century, from China. Powder made its first appearance in Europe in the fourteenth century, and it has been used in firearms and for blasting ever since. It is a mixture of charcoal, sulphur, and saltpeter (nitrate of potash, KNO_3). For cheaper blasting powders sodium nitrate may be used in place of saltpeter.

For charcoal light wood—willow or alder—is burned at a low temperature. Saltpeter is not found native in quantity and was long made by mixing organic material such as straw with wood ashes in piles and keeping these moist so as to promote decay. Bacteria converted the nitrogen of the straw into nitric acid, which in turn combined with the potash in the wood ashes. The nitrate was leached out of the mass with water, and the solution evaporated and crystallized. This primitive method supplied the saltpeter for our Revolutionary War powder, and was used by the South during the Civil War.

The modern method of making saltpeter uses sodium nitrate imported from Chile, or made synthetically, and potassium chloride:

$$NaNO_3 + KCl = KNO_3 + NaCl$$

The three ingredients of black powder are crushed separately to a coarse powder, and weighed into parcels (300 pounds saltpeter, 40 pounds sulphur and 60 pounds charcoal) for transportation to the grinding mill. The manufacture is hazardous; a rigid rule of safety is not to perform two different operations in the same place, and the materials which constitute the normal charge of a powder mill are not brought together until they reach the pan of the grinding unit.

The grinding mill in universal use consists of a flat cast-iron pan set in masonry. Its low sides are of wood, and through the center is a vertical shaft. Sliding on the shaft is a horizontal axle that carries two wide-tired cast-iron wheels, each weighing about four tons. The electric motor, starting switch, gearing, and clutch are all located at a distance, behind a barricade, so that no one is in the wheelhouse during starting, in fact during operation, of the mill.

The several ingredients are dumped in the pan, spread with a wooden shovel, and thoroughly wetted down. Then the motor is started, and the verticle shaft begins to revolve, causing the wheels to roll around on the flat pan. A plow follows each wheel, turning the pasty material over, in front of the following wheel. This combined grinding and kneading continues until the mass has been ground extremely fine and the several ingredients are thoroughly intermixed.

The heavy doughlike product from the grinding mill is then

transported to the press house, where a hydraulic press forms it into cakes about a foot square and an inch thick. The cakes are stacked in open piles to dry in the air. After drying to the proper degree, they are *corned* (crushed to granules) in a roller mill. This consists of a series of bronze rolls which revolve very slowly. The granules are then screened and sorted into several commercial sizes, or "grades."

Each size is then transported to the *glazing* house and charged into a rotating wooden barrel; a small amount of graphite is added, and rolled onto the surface of the grains. This coating renders the grains of powder somewhat more waterproof. Once again the grains are sized through screens.

The finest-grained powder is used in fuse; the medium, in cartridges and fireworks; the coarsest for blasting.

The chemistry of its explosion is:
$$2\,KNO_3 + 3\,C + S = K_2S + N_2 + 3\,CO_2$$
A small amount of the sulphur may burn to SO_2, and the potassium sulphide may be partly oxidized to sulphate.

It will be noted that black powder produces gas only to the extent of some 40 per cent of its weight—more than half of the residue being solid and contributing nothing to the explosive effect. It is fired by a flame, either from a fuse or from a cap. Though the temperature created is quite high, it burns slowly for an explosive; and the small amount of gas produced gives this powder one of the lowest ratings among explosives.

Smokeless powder is, from the chemical viewpoint, a wholly different explosive. There are two varieties: the Europeans use a nitroglycerine, we a nitrocellulose powder. The demand for longer range is forcing the use of small amounts of nitroglycerine in the newer American powders.

Nitrocellulose (see page 161) is the principal constituent of both European and American smokeless, and is made like nitrocellulose for celluloid. Stronger acids and higher temperatures are used in nitration, as the "pyro" used in powders contains 12.5 to 13 per cent nitrogen. The boiling, alkali washes, and the disintegration are all carried out with the greatest care. For the American type of powder, the nitrocellulose is centrifuged to remove most of the water; more is then expressed in a hydraulic press, and the last of the water displaced by alcohol while still in the press. The pyro cotton is then dissolved in ether in a heavy dough mixing machine: it does not go into solution, but forms a jellylike mass. Kneading is continued until not a trace of fiber remains. This jelly is then pressed into a block, and the block fed to a macaroni machine which extrudes long thin rods. The rods are pressed into a cake, and the extrusion repeated. These rods are cut by machine into the final grain size. The grained powder is collected in small cars and taken to a drying room where the solvent is evaporated and recovered for reuse. The dried powder is in firm hornlike grains, and these are thrown into water to dissolve out the last traces of solvent. After final air-drying, the several batches of like-sized grain are blended for utmost uniformity, and packed for shipment to the loading plants.

In the European practice, the alcohol-wet pyro cotton is mixed with acetone and nitroglycerine, and then reduced to gel form. Depending on the particular service, 20 to 35 per cent nitroglycerine is added. The milling is done on rolls similar to those used in the rubber industry, which are safer for the purpose than a kneading machine.

To insure stability over long periods of storage, about 0.5 per cent of diphenylamine, $(C_6H_5)_2NH$, is added in the dough mixer. Some powders contain a plasticizer, usually an organic ester, to facilitate extrusion and graining.

Smokeless powder is also ignited or fired by a flame, usually from a cap. The design, and size, of the powder grain varies with the size of the gun in which it is to be used. Small arms use fine-grained powders, but the grain for large guns may be an inch in diameter and several inches long. Such large grains are perforated longitudinally with a number of small holes. They fire both on the surface and in the holes; and these canals enlarge through combustion, exposing greater surface, so that the burning becomes more and more rapid. Thus, as the projectile moves down the gun barrel the volume of gas behind it increases at an ever faster rate, and the pressure, too. This may reach 20,000 to 30,000 pounds per square inch.

High explosives are divided into two general classes: commercial and military. The classes are equally powerful, but military explosives have certain requirements in which they differ from the commercial group.

Sensitivity is an important property of all high explosives. It is measured by the force of the blow required to detonate (set off) the explosive, and is determined by letting fall a weight of 2 kilograms (4.5 pounds) from increasing heights on a sample of explosive resting on a steel block. The minimum height causing explosion is the measure of sensitivity. Commercial explosives are handled under well determined conditions and in accordance with definite rules. In battle such care is not possible. Therefore high explosives for military use are relatively insensitive. A rifle bullet may be fired through a case of military explosive and have no effect; but not through a case of commercial explosive—dynamite, for example. Military explosives are much more expensive than commercial.

Nitroglycerine is the base of most commercial high explosives. It itself is probably the most powerful of all. The power of an explosive, called *brisance,* is determined by detonating 10 grams (one-third ounce) inside a lead cylinder, and measuring the expansion of the cylinder after the explosion. The lead cylinder will not shatter, and its expansion is easily measured. It is customary to record brisance on an arbitrary scale with nitroglycerine as 100.

The sensitivity of nitroglycerine is very low; that is, a low fall of the weight will detonate it. Handling is therefore very hazardous. It cannot be transported on a railroad. Its principal use as an explosive is for shooting oil wells. It is a liquid and is loaded into tall slender cans which are carefully lowered into the well. When the charge has been placed, a steel weight is dropped down, the shock setting off the explosive.

Nitroglycerine is made from glycerine and a mixture of nitric and sulphuric acids:

$$C_3H_5(OH)_3 + 3\ HNO_3 = C_3H_5(NO_3)_3 + 3\ H_2O$$

The sulphuric acid is added only to take care of the water produced in the nitration, and enable the reaction to run to completion. The glycerine, known as nitration grade, is 99 per cent pure, 1 per cent water. An excess of nitric acid is used—the usual mixture being 600 pounds of glycerine, and 4,000 pounds of mixed acid containing 35 per cent nitric acid, 62 per cent sulphuric acid, and 3 per cent water.

The apparatus is rather simple. On the top floor of the nitration building are separate tanks for the glycerine and the acid. Just below them is a lead-lined tank provided with an agitator and lead cooling coils through which cold brine from a refrigerating unit circulates, if very cold water is not available.

The acid charge is run into this tank, the agitator started, and the glycerine follows in a very slow stream. The temperature must not rise above 65° Fahrenheit. If the temperature cannot be controlled the whole charge must be dumped immediately into a large tank of water immediately under the nitration pot, for an explosion is imminent.

In about forty-five minutes the nitration is completed, and the batch is dropped into a washing tank below. The oily nitroglycerine separates from the excess acid, which is drawn off and recovered. Water is added to wash the acid out of the nitroglycerine, which is agitated by a jet of compressed air. After several water washes, a weak solution of sodium carbonate neutralizes any remaining acid. More washes with fresh water follow until no acid or alkali can be detected. The product is then loaded into cans and transferred to the powder or the dynamite plants.

Dynamite, in various forms, is the principal commercial high explosive. Nitroglycerine is too sensitive for general use; but if it is mixed with an inert material, such as wood flour, the mixture will be much less sensitive, and can be moved about—under rigid regulations—with considerable safety.

Dynamites consist principally of nitroglycerine, sodium or ammonium nitrate, and an absorbent such as wood flour. There are many grades on the market, carrying from 75 per cent down to 20 per cent nitroglycerine. The safety powders used in coal mining are low in nitroglycerine and high in ammonium nitrate, which is also a high explosive, but can be detonated only if mixed with another explosive.

Gelatine dynamite is made by mixing 10 per cent nitrocellulose with nitroglycerine, forming a jellylike mass. There is no gelatine in it. It ranks next to nitroglycerine in brisance, and is less sensitive, though more so than the regular dynamites.

Regular and gelatine dynamites are made in much the same way as black powder. The mill consists of the pan and rolls, much smaller and lighter, and wholly of wood. The several ingredients are charged into the wooden pan and mixed under the rolls. The resulting doughlike mass is packed in paper cartridges of varying sizes; the diameter must fit the drill hole, the length being adequate for the designated weight of the stick. Regulations prescribed that twenty-five or fifty pounds of sticks shall be packed in a box. The paper used is the so-called cartridge paper, waterproofed with a mixture of rosin and paraffine.

Dynamite will freeze at a low temperature; when nitroglycerine is solid it is a very uncertain and dangerous substance, and thawing of frozen dynamite has caused many accidents. To prevent freezing, dinitrobenzene or nitroglycol is incorporated into dynamite. These antifreeze compounds have added greatly to the safety in handling it in cold weather.

Nitrostarch can be substituted for nitroglycerine. It is a solid material made from starch and mixed acid in much the same way as nitrocellulose. While very effective as an explosive, it is troublesome to manufacture, for it is more difficult to wash than the liquid nitroglycerine.

Dynamites are graded as 20, 40, 60 per cent, etc. The percentages indicate the effectiveness of the grade as compared to nitroglycerine. That is, a 40 per cent dynamite is about equivalent in blasting power to four-tenths of the same weight of nitroglycerine.

Commercial explosives of quite different kind are made from potassium chlorate and an organic nitro compound. In the United States they are little used; in foreign lands they are called cheddites. For one of these, finely ground potassium chlorate, $KClO_3$, is mixed with dinitrotoluene, $CH_3C_6H_3(NO_2)_2$, and castor oil, and packed in cartridges. It is a very powerful explosive.

Military high explosives are of an altogether different character. One of the first (now largely obsolete) was *guncotton*. It is a nitrocellulose of high nitrogen content, and is compressed into cakes and blocks while wet. This highly compressed material can be exploded with a powerful detonator even when wet. It is very insensitive to shock and has about 85 per cent the brisance of nitroglycerine. It is bulky and is not adapted to loading in shells. Its principal use was in naval torpedoes and in the demolition bombs used by army engineers.

Trinitrotoluene, or TNT, $CH_3C_6H_2(NO_2)_3$, is the most important military high explosive. It is quite insensitive, yet has a brisance about two-thirds that of nitroglycerine. The melting point is quite low, only 185° Fahrenheit, and it can be safely melted and cast into shells and bombs. In a shell this is very important, for the explosive with which it is loaded must not be dislodged by the shock of firing; otherwise, the shell will become unbalanced and accuracy of fire will be impossible. Furthermore, TNT can withstand, without detonating, the shock of the shell's striking the target—an invaluable property for naval projectiles, since it enables the explosion to be timed after penetration of a ship's armor.

The manufacture is not difficult. Toluene can be nitrated to the tri- stage in a single operation; but it is considered as less hazardous to accomplish the nitrations in three stages: first, to mononitrotoluene, $CH_3C_6H_4(NO_2)$; second, to dinitrotoluene, $CH_3C_6H_3(NO_2)_2$; and finally to the trinitrotoluene. Each of these steps can be controlled by varying the strength of the mixed acid, the temperature, and the time of nitration. The mono- and dinitrotoluenes are intermediates in the dye industry, and are produced in quantity in peacetimes. Trinitrotoluene has no other use than as an explosive. The nitration of toluene is carried out much like that of glycerine; but, because toluene is quite volatile, the nitration kettles are closed.

Ammonium nitrate is an explosive of rather low brisance. It is made by adding ammonia to nitric acid, both in water solution;

the water is evaporated, and the nitrate crystals dried. It is quite insensitive to shock and therefore difficult to detonate even with the heaviest blasting caps; but it has the advantage of facility of manufacture.

It is a cheap compound to manufacture; in fact it is largely used in some countries as a fertilizer material. Most explosive plants produce large quantities of spent nitrating acid. The spent acid carries sulphuric acid, nitric acid, and water, and is so diluted and contaminated that it can no longer be safely used in further nitration. The nitric acid can be recovered by blowing steam through it and condensing the nitric vapors. The sulphuric goes to sulphuric acid concentrators, where it is concentrated and sold to many other industries. Ammonium nitrate is prepared by neutralizing the recovered nitric acid.

Ammonium nitrate is added to dynamites, both regular and gelatine. The nitroglycerine is readily detonated, and the shock of its explosion is strong enough to set off the admixed ammonium nitrate. Similarly in military explosives, ammonium nitrate is melted with TNT and the mixture cast into bombs. The explosive amatol, used in the largest quantity of all military high explosives, is a cast mixture of 80 per cent ammonium nitrate and 20 per cent TNT. To insure its explosion a booster charge is inserted in the central axis of the bomb.

Trinitro aniline, TNA, Picramide, $NH_2C_6H_2(NO_2)_3$, is made by nitrating aniline. It is used in a small way in booster charges and in primers. Of much greater importance is tetranitro methyl aniline, Tetryl, $(NO_2)_3C_6H_2N(CH_3)NO_2$, an explosive of low sensitivity but extremely great brisance. Methyl aniline is first made in an autoclave from methyl alcohol and an aniline salt. The methyl aniline, $C_6H_5NH(CH_3)$, is then nitrated to the Tetryl, as above. It is used for booster charges, and for loading medium-caliber shells, for it has great power of fragmentation.

A high explosive once in general use, and still preferred by the Russian armies, is *picric acid,* trinitrophenol, $(NO_2)_3C_6H_2OH$. Its manufacture is very simple: phenol is mixed with concentrated sulphuric acid to form the phenol sulphonate, $HOC_6H_4HSO_3$. This is diluted with water and placed in an agitated vessel. Moderately strong nitric acid is run in. When the nitration is complete the vessel and its contents are cooled, and the picric acid crystallizes out. The crystals are separated and washed in a centrifuge, and packed wet for shipment. They must be dried before melting and casting into the shell. Picric acid has about the same sensitivity and brisance as TNT. Its disadvantage lies in its corrosive nature. It attacks iron and steel, and the resulting salts are very sensitive to shock. The interiors of shells and bombs must be enameled before they are charged with picric acid.

The high explosive Hexite or Hexogen, trimethylene trinitramine, has recently become of great importance. Germany has long used it because of shortage of toluene. It is extremely powerful and rather insensitive, but is very hazardous to manufacture. From ammonia and formaldehyde—both of synthetic origin, steam and coal being the raw materials—hexamethylene tetramine is made:

$$6 \text{ HCHO} + 4 \text{ NH}_3 = \text{C}_6\text{H}_{12}\text{N}_4 + 6 \text{ H}_2\text{O}$$

The manufacture is very simple, and the product is used in large quantities in the rubber and the plastics industries. It is nitrated to Hexite in several stages. The explosive compound is:

$$\begin{array}{c}
\text{NO}_2 \\
| \\
\text{N—CH}_2 \\
\diagup \qquad \diagdown \\
\text{CH}_2 \qquad\qquad \text{N—NO}_2 \\
\diagdown \qquad \diagup \\
\text{N—CH}_2 \\
| \\
\text{NO}_2
\end{array}$$

Another explosive that can be made wholly from synthetic materials is Penthrite, a tetranitrate of pentaerythrite, $\text{C(CH}_2\text{NO}_3)_4$. The pentaerythrite is made from two aldehydes—formaldehyde and acetaldehyde—and then nitrated. It has been used for some years in limited quantity in Central Europe as a commercial explosive. Its brisance is extremely high, but the sensitivity is low for military use. It is used in land mines.

A simple fuse may be used for firing propellent powders, but a percussion cap is more convenient. This is a small cup of copper, containing a charge of a very sensitive explosive that is detonated by shock, usually administered by a firing pin. Mixed in with the very sensitive explosive are compounds that ignite easily and produce a flame which is projected into the mass of powder in the cartridge or shell case. In large guns the powder is loaded in bags, and an intense flame is merely projected into the powder chamber of the gun.

The most widely used detonating compound is fulminate of mercury, $Hg(CNO)_2$. Mercury is dissolved in nitric acid, and the mercuric nitrate is treated with alcohol. A tiny bit is placed in the bottom of the copper capsule, and covered with a flame-producing material. This may be one of various sulphides, or black powder.

Most high explosives will burn if ignited by a flame, and their maximum explosive effect will not be developed. But if they receive a very severe shock, a vibratory wave of decomposition is set up which causes an instantaneous rearrangement of the atoms. The carbon and hydrogen unite with the oxygen that was attached to the nitrogen. A great deal of heat is set free, and the gases that result from oxidation—CO_2, CO, H_2O, N_2, NO, N_2O_4—are at a high temperature and under tremendous pressure.

The shock is derived from a primer, and for high explosives larger quantities of fulminate are required than for powders. The caps are of two kinds: percussion, intended to be struck by a firing pin; and blasting, fired either by a fuse or by an electric current. The electric cap contains a short length of fine platinum wire bedded in the explosive charge of the cap, and connected to the two leads. When an electric current is passed through the cap, the platinum is heated to redness and sets off the fulminate. Lead azide, PbN_6, is used in percussion caps in place of fulminate. The larger caps often contain small booster charges of Tetryl, nitro-mannitol, and other sensitive explosive compounds.

In large shells and bombs the detonating cap fires a booster charge of a powerful explosive, which in turn detonates the main charge. This saves the expensive detonator, and produces a better

A SYNTHETIC RESIN KETTLE

Discharge outlet on floor below

A DYNAMITE MIXING PAN
Visitors not permitted during operation

detonation. This booster charge is placed in a tube buried in the center of the main charge of high explosive.

There are always tales of new and devastating explosives suddenly coming to light. The explosive chemist already knows which combinations have explosive properties, and it is most unlikely that new compounds, with hitherto unsuspected characteristics, will suddenly appear. The character of the explosives in use may change, as new types of service arise, or conditions which permit the use of more sensitive explosives appear, or a shortage of raw materials requires change in source of supply. One should be very skeptical of reports of new and terrible explosives, developed in secret, and suddenly to be hurled upon an unsuspecting world. The thermodynamics of the various chemical groupings are rather well understood, and the range of what is possible in explosives is fairly well established.

CHAPTER XV

PIGMENTS AND DYES

Color plays a most important part in nature and in the drama of life. Tinted drawings are found on the walls of caves inhabited by the earliest man. The Old Testament speaks frequently of colored robes. Among the most primitive peoples we find the gayest hues: the natives of Equatorial Africa wear the most brilliant colors; the Indians of the southwestern United States, living in the drear surroundings of the desert, make colorful pottery and textiles. Today, thousands of pigments and dyes are available to meet this inextinguishable desire for color, and new ones are constantly being invented in our laboratories.

The name "pigment," or "color" (in commerce, "dry color"), is applied to an insoluble powder such as tints paints, enamels, inks, and the like. Dyes, on the other hand, are soluble materials used for coloring textiles, paper, lacquer, and stains. The distinction is not absolute, for some dyes may be used as colors, and then they are fixed in an insoluble base. The lake colors are a common example.

Nature provided the first pigments and dyes: The mineral oxide of iron is red; copper and nickel salts are characteristically green. The verdigris or patina on a copper roof is a basic carbonate of copper. Because native minerals have been long exposed to the ravages of the weather, their colors are usually quite permanent, and these, after fine grinding, can be used as pigments.

But man is not always content with what nature has given him. He wants more variety, more brilliance, better quality. A large branch of the chemical industry is devoted to supplying a wide variety of pigments and dyes, only a few of which can be mentioned here.

White lead, basic carbonate of lead, $Pb(OH)_2 \cdot 2\ PbCO_3$, has been used as a pigment for more than two thousand years. The most modern process for making it uses a stream of molten lead atomized into a fine lead powder by a jet of air. The powder is put into a revolving drum with a small amount of acetic acid, and gases from a burning coke fire are blown through the drum to supply carbonic acid. The acetic acid attacks the lead and forms lead acetate, which the carbon dioxide immediately precipitates as the basic carbonate, and at the same time regenerates the acetic acid, so that only a small amount of the latter is required to treat a large quantity of lead. The revolution of the drum grinds the insoluble carbonate off the lead particles, and keeps a fresh surface exposed. The chemical reactions are:

$$Pb + 2\ CH_3COOH = Pb(CH_3COO)_2 + H_2$$
$$3\ Pb(CH_3COO)_2 + CO_2 + H_2O =$$
$$Pb(OH)_2 \cdot 2\ PbCO_3 + 6\ CH_3COOH$$

Another very common white pigment, but of fairly modern origin, is *zinc oxide,* ZnO, made by burning vapor of metallic zinc in a current of air. The oxide is filtered out of the gas stream by woolen bags in the shape of long pendent tubes.

Lithopone, another white pigment, has a rather indefinite composition, for it is formulated in many varieties. A solution of barium sulphide, BaS, is precipitated by a solution of zinc sulphate, $ZnSO_4$, the proportions for the several varieties being altered between certain narrow limits. It is used extensively for inside flat paints, rarely for outdoor use.

Titanium dioxide, titanium white, TiO_2, is replacing white lead as a white pigment. Ilmenite, the ore containing oxides of titanium and iron, is ground fine and dissolved in strong sulphuric acid. The sulphate of iron crystallizes out and is discarded. The remaining solution contains titanic acid, H_2TiO_3, dissolved in the strong acid; it precipitates as titanium dioxide, TiO_2, when the solution is diluted and boiled. Many of the best titanium pigments consist of mixtures of titanium dioxide and barium or calcium sulphates. Titanium pigments are not poisonous and have greater hiding power than other whites.

Two oxides of lead are used in the paint industry: *litharge,* PbO, and *red lead,* Pb_3O_4. They are made by passing air over highly heated molten lead.

Lead chromate, chrome yellow, $PbCrO_4$, is precipitated from a solution of a soluble lead salt, such as lead nitrate, by a solution of sodium dichromate:

$$2 Pb (NO_3)_2 + Na_2Cr_2O_7 + H_2O =$$
$$2 PbCrO_4 + 2 NaNO_3 + 2 HNO_3$$

Zinc chromate, $ZnCrO_4$, is made in the same manner. It is a good priming coating on metals.

Prussian blue is made by adding a solution of ferrous sulphate to a solution of sodium ferrocyanide or potassium ferrocyanide. A light-colored, slimy ferrocyanide of iron precipitates; this is washed lightly to remove some of the sulphates of the alkali of the ferrocyanide. The slimy precipitate is oxidized to a ferricyanide by nitric acid, or by potassium chlorate. The blue ferricyanide of iron is not a definite chemical compound, but approximates the formula $Fe_4[Fe (CN)_6]_3$. By skillful manipulation various shades of blue, and also blues with bronze and red undertones, can be produced. Mixed with chrome yellow, it gives an excellent green, one of whose uses is to color the ink used in printing our paper money.

The early *dyes* were all obtained from plants, barks, flowers, and animals. In biblical times a purple dye was produced from a species of shellfish found along the shores of the Mediterranean. The early settlers in America boiled walnut hulls in water to make a brown dye. Logwood is still imported in large quantities from Central America for its dye content.

But most of the present-day dyes are synthetic products of the organic chemical industry. Some of the synthetic dyes are exact chemical duplicates of natural ones, notably indigo and alizarin; but most synthetic dyes are not duplicated in nature.

Dyes are complex organic compounds, and their chemistry is very involved. There is no simple classification of dyes in universal use. For commercial purposes a combination system is used, partly based on chemical composition, partly on method of application. What will constitute a commercial dye is largely a matter of trial and error. Many organic compounds possess color, but unless this color can be fixed on a textile fiber they are not classed as dyes. Even beyond this, there are certain standards of fastness they must meet.

Fastness is, however, a relative term, and must be further qualified. There is fastness to light, to perspiration and other body fluids, to laundering and to dry cleaning. Some dyes are fast to light and not to perspiration; that is, such might be used on a drape, but not on a dress fabric. Many laundries use strong bleaching agents which affect dyes. Dyes for wash goods must be selected with this in mind. Perspiration-resistant colors present still another problem; so do bright sunlight and artificial lighting. In commerce, every dye carries specifications as to the degree of fastness to each of the several exposures.

A dye contains a color-giving group of atoms, called a "chromophore." There are about a dozen well recognized chromophores. A characteristic one is the *azo* group, —N=N—. The chromophore may be attached to two aromatic groups, or to one aromatic and one aliphatic group. In the more deeply colored dyes, the chromophore may be repeated one or more times. Dyes also contain auxochromes which assist in attaching them to fabrics. Auxochromes are such groups as amide, —NH_2, and hydroxy, —OH. The problem in dye chemistry is to couple up these several groups in proper sequence—that is, to create the proper molecular structure.

The raw materials of the synthetic dye industry are benzene, toluene, and xylene from the light oils of the coke oven; naphthalene, anthracene, and carbazole, $C_6H_4NHC_6H_4$, from coal tar. From these raw materials several hundred *intermediates* are made by various chemical manipulations, and the intermediates are coupled together to make the final dye. Large quantities of mineral acids, alkalies, halogens, and salts are used in the production of the intermediates and the dyes. Sometimes more than a hundred pounds of raw materials and reagents make only a single pound of dye. Some of the processes require as many as three dozen distinct chemical operations.

The application of the dye to the fabric usually requires additional chemical assistants. Some dyes must undergo reduction before they can be put into solution; some require development—much like the photographic film. Others will not attach themselves to a fiber without an intermediate, or *mordant*. Certain cotton dyes require that the textile be soaked in a solution of tannic acid, $(HO)_3C_6H_2 \cdot CO_2C_6H_2(OH)_2COOH$, and then in a solution of potassium antimonyl tartrate, $KSbOC_4H_4O_6$, which precipitates as a tannate on the fiber. Then follows the dye bath. Chrome colors are fixed after a bath of potassium or sodium chromate.

The *vat* dyes are the fastest and most permanent of all the dye groups. The name is derived from the method of application. These dyes are insoluble in water, and must be reduced by a strong reducing agent, such as sodium hydrosulphite, $Na_2S_2O_4$, in order to make them soluble. In the reduced form the dyes are colorless and dissolve readily in a dilute alkaline solution. This is applied to the fabric. A chemical oxidizing agent, even air in some cases, restores the color to the dye in the fabric. Indigo is a typical example of a vat dye. The name comes from an old practice of reducing the dye in a tub by the fermentation of bran or molasses; it is now done almost instantly by a chemical reducing agent.

Indigo was originally prepared from the indigo plant of India. Indigo white, $C_{16}H_{12}N_2O_2$, a water-soluble compound, was leached out of its leaves and stems. The solution was then violently agitated in air, which oxidized the indigo white to the insoluble indigo blue, $C_{16}H_{10}N_2O_2$. This was filtered out, pressed into cakes, and shipped to the dyeing plants, where it was reduced back to the soluble white, applied to the fabric, and again oxidized to the blue. Today indigo is a synthetic product, and is not only cheaper but of higher quality and greater uniformity of color and tinctorial strength.

There are several commercial methods of making indigo. One process starts with aniline; and since this enters into so many dyes, a description of its manufacture is in order. Aniline, aminobenzene, $C_6H_5NH_2$, is made from benzene, C_6H_6. The benzene is first nitrated with a mixed acid to produce nitrobenzene, $C_6H_5NO_2$. The liquid nitro compound is insoluble in water, and can be washed free of the acid nitrating mixture, and distilled to insure purity of product, which is essential in the manufacture of any dye.

The nitrobenzene is then placed in an agitated vessel with a small amount of hydrochloric acid, and a large quantity of iron borings. The iron and acid react to produce hydrogen, which at the instant of formation reduces the nitrobenzene to aniline:

$$C_6H_5NO_2 + 3 H_2 = C_6H_5NH_2 + 2 H_2O$$

The hydrochloric acid is regenerated so that only a small amount is required; the iron forms an oxide, Fe_3O_4, and after sintering can be sent back to the blast furnace for resmelting. The aniline is separated from the oxide of iron, and is purified by distillation. Aniline is very poisonous, and its preparation and handling require extreme care.

To make indigo, the aniline is reacted with chlor-acetic acid to make the intermediate, phenylglycine:

$$C_6H_5NH_2 + CH_2ClCOOH = C_6H_5NHCH_2COOH + HCl$$

This intermediate is then fused with sodium amide, $NaNH_2$, to produce the intermediate, indoxyl:

$$C_6H_5NHCH_2COOH + NaNH_2 =$$
$$C_6H_4NHCH_2CO + NaOH + NH_3$$

When indoxyl is heated in an alkaline solution two molecules condense to a molecule of indigo:

$$2 C_6H_4NHCH_2CO = C_6H_4NHCOC:COCNHC_6H_4 + 2 H_2$$

Indigo is used as such for dyeing, but it is also converted into a number of derivatives by adding chlorine, sulphur, the methyl group, etc. These derivatives have different coloring properties. In the dye industry, the production of indigo is looked upon as a simple operation.

A great many vat dyes of excellent color and fastness are made from anthracene (see page 64). The triple ring in the anthracene molecule lends itself to a variety of condensations with various chemical groups. The *Indanthrenes,* which are the best of the "vats," exhibit an interlocking of the basic hexagon rings almost like the tiles on a floor. For example, Indanthrene Violet R Extra, $C_{36}H_{16}O_2$, has the constitution:

The *sulphur* dyes are not brilliant, but they are very fast. They are so complex that little is known about their constitution. Many organic compounds when fused with sulphur and sodium sulphide acquire color. They are insoluble in water, and for application are dissolved in a solution of sodium sulphide, Na_2S. This solution, being alkaline, cannot be used on wool, for alkaline solutions destroy the fiber; hence the sulphur dyes are used only on cotton. The most important is sulphur black, long used for dyeing stockings and other cottons demanding a very fast dye to laundering. Sulphur black is made by fusing dinitrophenol with sodium sulphide and sulphur. The production of the sulphur dyes is an art, for no two manufacturers produce dyes of exactly the same composition, though each may give equally good service.

The *azo* colors are very brilliant dyes, though somewhat fugitive (not fast). They are all processed in about the same manner, and out of a wide variety of intermediates. Their application to fabrics differs with the several dyes. Some are produced directly on the fabric. The azos are characterized by the chromophore, —N=N—, two atoms of nitrogen coupled with a double bond, each atom possessing a free valence enabling it to combine with a variety of intermediates, both of the aliphatic and of the aromatic series, sometimes both in the same dye.

The first step in the production of an azo dye is to convert an amide compound, as for example paranitraniline, $NH_2C_6H_4NO_2$ (this is a nitro compound of aniline), into a diazo compound by reacting it with sodium nitrite, $NaNO_2$, in an acid bath:

$$NH_2C_6H_4NO_2 + NaNO_2 + 2\ HCl =$$
$$NO_2C_6H_4N:NCl + NaCl + 2\ H_2O$$

This azo compound may then be coupled with beta naphthol, $C_{10}H_7OH$:

$$NO_2C_6H_4N:NCl + C_{10}H_7OH = NO_2C_6H_4N:NC_{10}H_6OH + HCl$$

The result is a pigment called para-red. It is the bright red so familiar on harvesting tools, and so common in outdoor lithographic inks. When textiles are to be colored by this red, the fabric is placed in the coupling bath with the two intermediates, and the above reaction forms the color directly on the textile fibers themselves.

Beta naphthol and its numerous sulphonates, combined with diazotized anilines, toluidines, and like amines, are the intermediates for a long list of most varicolored azo dyes. What may be a complete dye can be further diazotized and again coupled with another intermediate. The azo series seems to be without limit.

There are more than a thousand commercial dyes. The older and more fugitive are constantly being displaced by newer and faster ones. The finished products come on the market in the form of pastes, very carefully diluted with an inert salt, such as sodium sulphate. The pastes contain from 80 per cent down to 20 per cent of actual dye, and each grade is most carefully standardized as to shade and tinctorial power.

Most dyes are composed of the elements carbon, nitrogen, hydrogen, sulphur, chlorine. Three of these are colorless, and the other two enter into many combinations that are white; that is, color is not a characteristic property. Many of the compounds of these five elements are white, or colorless. In the dye, certain combinations of these elements have the property of absorbing all light except one single tint, or wave length; this is reflected and transmitted to the human eye as a recognized color. The dye chemist must rearrange these atoms, which he cannot see, into patterns that reflect the color desired, and at the same time eliminate all groupings that would interfere, or even send out an undesired color. His methods of synthesis are a series of additions and subtractions—not of figures, but of atomic groupings.

Paints, Varnishes, and Lacquers. Ordinary paint consists of three ingredients: the pigment, defining the color; a "vehicle," or oily constituent, to permit spreading and insure adherence; and a "dryer," to facilitate hardening. The bulk of the pigment is white lead or zinc oxide, or both, tinted with any of the many dry colors. The vehicle is some form of drying oil, such as linseed oil, which on exposure to air takes up oxygen (having two double bonds in its molecular structure) and hardens into a resinous material. The dryer is to hasten this oxidation.

Cheap paints may use other oils alone or as adulterants of linseed oil. To facilitate spreading of the paint as it is applied, a thinner may be added. In the better paints this is turpentine, which comes from the southern pine tree. In cheap paints the thinner is often a light petroleum oil.

Dryers are made by boiling manganese oxide, or cobalt oxide, with linseed oil. Chemically they are manganese or cobalt linoleates, of an indefinite composition. They act as a catalyst to pass the oxygen of the air to the linseed oil. High-gloss paints contain a little varnish; for flat paints, the light petroleum oils are added. The synthetic resins are finding their way into paint, and add to the durability; but too much addition makes brushing-out difficult.

Varnishes are liquids without pigment and are used for preservative and ornamental purposes. Their number is legion. The old-style varnish was made by melting a natural gum or resin, such as kauri, in a kettle, adding hot linseed oil, and cooking the two together. Turpentine is used to thin the batch to brushing consistency. Before packaging, a dryer may be added. Hard resins are used in making spar and furniture varnishes, since these are subject to unusual wear. The modern varnishes contain larger proportions of synthetic resins. Very quick-drying varnishes contain tung oil in place of part of the linseed oil. The tung-oil molecule contains three double bonds which facilitate quicker hardening. In printing inks linseed-oil varnish carries the pigment; these must be very quick-drying and have large quantities of cobalt dryer or, even better, a naphthenic compound derived from petroleum.

Lacquers differ from paints and varnishes in that they dry not by oxidation, but by the evaporation of a solvent. They are usually pigmented, and contain resins (natural or synthetic), a series of plasticizers, and the solvent. A soluble form of nitrocellulose is incorporated in many of them. The evaporation of the light, volatile solvent tends to produce minute pores or craters in the finish, but the plasticizers prevent this. As the solvent evaporates, they keep the lacquer plastic so that any craters that may form quickly disappear. Plasticizers are higher-boiling esters, such as ethyl acetate, $C_2H_5OOCCH_3$; butyl acetate, $C_4H_9OOCCH_3$; and dibutyl phthalate, $(C_4H_9OOC)_2C_6H_4$. The solvents are benzene, toluene, and light petroleum oils.

Because lacquers dry very fast, they should be applied by spraying. They are waterproof, and therefore do not give good service on wood, for any moisture entering beneath the coat of lacquer tends to make the lacquer scale off. They are generally baked on metals, in ovens or under infrared lamps. They have been of inestimable value to the automobile industry, where a complete finishing takes a few hours at most. The newer lacquers containing synthetic resins have remarkable resistance to sun and weather.

Hundreds of chemists are attempting to find more durable finishes. Sunlight and weather destroy the ordinary paint vehicles in too short a time, causing the paint to chalk and crack. Manufacturers of white wares want better retention of color. Industry insists on ever faster setting and drying so that production can be speeded. The age when a buggy was held in the paint shop for three weeks or a month is past; three hours is now too long.

CHAPTER XVI

DRUGS, PHARMACEUTICALS, AND VITAMINS

Life is a complex of chemical reactions. Vegetable foods are transformed into animal tissues; carbon dioxide and water, into carbohydrates; nitrogen, into amino acids. In the healthy body, *metabolism* (the chemical transformation of food into body structure and energy) is a natural process. But interruption or derangement of the normal reactions makes medicine necessary; and medicines are made by chemists. The physician employs many chemical tests to confirm his diagnosis; he gives chemical products to assist Nature in making for recovery.

The terms *drug, medicine,* and *pharmaceutical* have been used indiscriminately to designate substances applied to the prevention or cure of disease. For clarity, *medicine* will be used here for an actual prescription, which is usually a blended product; *drug,* for a natural product requiring little or no chemical preparation; and *pharmaceutical,* for a synthetic product of the chemical factory.

Antitoxins and *vaccines* belong in a special class.

Many common diseases are caused by bacteria and viruses. A bacterium is a living organism of rather complex chemical protein structure. It takes nourishment from its surrounding environment, reproducing with great rapidity, and discharges toxins, or poisons; and if enough bacteria excrete enough of these poisons into the blood of a human being he will become ill, and may die. Whether viruses are animal or vegetable, or possibly even only chemical compounds, has not been determined; they do reproduce themselves at a very alarming rate.

The blood stream of a normal healthy person carries certain compounds (antibodies) which destroy bacteria and viruses. If the

194

antibodies are present in sufficient numbers, they will kill the bacteria before they can multiply dangerously. This is what is meant by natural immunity. But disease gets a start if the number of antibodies is not sufficient to check the bacteria.

Fortunately, man has learned how to increase the number of antibodies quickly. This is accomplished by giving *antitoxins*, produced as follows:

An animal (usually a horse—but experience must determine the kind chosen) is isolated, and carefully examined over a period of time to see that it is healthy. Then it is inoculated with very small doses of living bacteria, which are destroyed by the antibodies present in its blood. The doses are slowly increased, and with them the antibodies increase. This continues until there are so many antibodies in the animal's blood that it is practically immune to the harmful bacteria.

Its blood is then drawn from time to time and processed. The unwanted parts are eliminated, and the serum (the part containing the antibodies) is concentrated, and carefully sterilized to make certain that it contains no bacteria. It is then tested for potency and packed in containers specially designed to hold a certain number of units, as measured on the potency scale. When this antitoxin is injected into a human blood stream the number of antibodies increases to an extent that insures the destruction of the infecting germ.

Each type of disease-producing bacteria requires its own antitoxin, prepared essentially in this way.

Whereas an antitoxin is used to cure, a *vaccine* is intended to immunize—that is, to prevent contraction of a disease.

The vaccines are prepared by growing bacteria in broth in dishes in a laboratory. When enough bacteria have been produced they are killed by heat, or by a germicide like formaldehyde. After purification and concentration, the mass of dead bacteria is ready for introduction into the blood stream of the person to be immunized. Here the dead bacteria are decomposed (autolyzed), and because the products of this decomposition are toxic to any living bacteria of the same breed that may get into the blood, the person immunized is free from infection. The immunity may be temporary or permanent.

A modified vaccine is the recently developed *toxoid,* in which the dead bacteria are decomposed in the laboratory and the products of decomposition are concentrated on such a carrier as aluminum hydroxide. This is then injected into the blood stream to produce immunization. Such extremely concentrated form makes small dosage possible, and thereby reduces the possibility of side reactions (ill effects).

It is not known how man discovered that certain plants would cure some of the ills of his body. Perhaps the knowledge came, in the very beginning, from watching animals. As experience accumulated the earliest physicians, proceeding wholly by trial and error, prepared a great many extracts, effusions, and elixirs from plants and animals. The alchemists devoted a great deal of time to haphazard preparations intended for medicines. Sometimes their concoctions worked as intended, and a surprisingly large number of drugs in today's pharmacy date from alchemistic times. In recent years a distinct branch of the chemical industry has developed, producing new chemical compounds for use as medicines. There are thousands of these pharmaceuticals, only a few of which can be discussed here.

Antiseptics are chemical compounds used to destroy the microorganisms that infect cuts and wounds, or cause infectious diseases. There are two classes: those that are employed in the absence, and those that are employed in the presence, of living tissue.

Soap is an old and rather effective antiseptic. Alcohol and an alcoholic solution of iodine—tincture of iodine—are used for disinfecting shallow wounds, or the skin before an incision is made. The tar acids—phenol, cresol, etc.—are widely used for disinfecting utensils, laundry, even whole buildings; but in surgery they are practically obsolete, because they can destroy living tissue. Formaldehyde has similar uses; also, in modified form, it can be given internally for a few specific ills.

Most mercury compounds have antiseptic properties. Mercuric chloride (corrosive sublimate), $HgCl_2$, has long been employed to disinfect instruments, utensils, and the hands—generally in water solution, one-half to one part chloride to one thousand parts of water. It is no longer used for treating wounds and incisions.

Chlorine is a very effective antiseptic but, because it is a gas, requires elaborate equipment for application. The water supplies of most cities are treated with chlorine to destroy typhoid and similar water-borne bacteria. The gas is released directly into water, the quantity depending on the degree of contamination (average, about one pound per two million pounds of water). The effect of the chlorine is greatly magnified if ammonia gas is simultaneously fed into the water stream.

For surgical use, chlorine is applied in the form of a solution of sodium hypochlorite, NaClO (Dakin's solution). This is not stable, and must be freshly prepared each time it is to be used. A stable proprietary compound, Chloramine T, $C_7H_7SO_2NClNa$, made from sodium hypochlorite and a derivative of toluene, is much more convenient and equally effective. Many organic compounds containing chlorine have antiseptic properties.

The most virulent infections are the diseases caused by living microorganisms in the blood stream; but the antiseptics just described cannot be put into the blood to destroy these, because they would also destroy vital living tissue, and the patient would die. Serums are used for a few such infections, but there are many diseases for which none has been developed. Serums cannot cope with great epidemics, because they take a long time to prepare, are very expensive, and (many of them) lose their potency on long storage. A pharmaceutical preparation that can destroy the invading organism has many advantages over the serum, and much chemical research has gone into synthesizing chemical products that will serve the purpose.

Many coal-tar dyes and their intermediates have germicidal properties, yet will not destroy living tissue. The German chemist Ehrlich sought and found a product that could be safely introduced into the blood stream, yet would destroy the spirochete that causes syphilis. He started with a number of compounds that were known to kill the germ but could not be tolerated by the patient;

and, after hundreds of trials, he succeeded in so modifying them chemically that they retained their germicidal property but, in the dosage required, would not poison the patient.

The syphilis spirochete is very resistant, and to destroy it requires a toxin as powerful as trivalent arsenic. But such an arsenic compound must be materially modified before it can be tolerated by a human being, particularly in the blood stream. After six hundred and six attempts Ehrlich produced such an arsenical preparation in his Salvarsan (chemically, arsphenamine), $C_{12}H_{12}As_2N_2O_2 \cdot 2$ HCl$\cdot 2$ H$_2$O. The toxic arsenic is tightly locked in this combination, and is liberated very slowly into the blood stream. The manufacture of Salvarsan is quite complicated and must be carried out in glass-lined apparatus shutting out all air. Extreme care must be exercised to insure purity. A later modification, neoarsphenamine, $NH_2OHC_6H_3As{:}AsC_6H_3OHNH(CH_2O)OSNa$, is now used more than the original Salvarsan; it can be injected intramuscularly with fewer undesirable secondary reactions.

One of man's worst scourges, malaria, is also caused by a particularly resistant parasite in the blood stream. Quinine, extracted from the bark of a tropical tree, was, for several centuries, the only remedy. The chemical formula of quinine is $C_{26}H_{24}N_2O_2$, and it has now been synthesized in the laboratory. The dried bark of the cinchona tree, cultivated on a large scale in Java, is ground with lime and caustic soda, and extracted with solvent naphtha. The quinine is next extracted from the solution with hot sulphuric acid, concentrated, and crystallized out as quinine sulphate on cooling.

Natural quinine is very effective; but large dosages are required, which few malaria sufferers can tolerate, and a substitute has long been desired.

The malaria parasite goes through two successive life stages in the blood. Quinine is effective against both. Two synthetic compounds have recently come from the laboratory (trade names Atabrine and Plasmochin), each specific against one of the stages, so that they are complementary to each other. Both compounds have the same nucleus, acridine, $C_6H_4CHC_6H_4N$, and this has a triple ring structure. Both contain a long straight-chain amino substituted hydrocarbon linked to the nucleus. Atabrine is further modified by containing methoxy, $CH_3O—$, and chlorine groups attached to the acridine ring, typical of the methods employed by the pharmaceutical chemist in modifying his poisonous organic groupings to give greater tolerance.

The cocci (globular) bacteria are responsible for many common diseases. There are many varieties: streptococcus, staphylococcus, pneumococcus, etc. There are thirty-odd varieties of pneumonia, and serums have been developed for most of them (each variety requiring a specific serum); but before using a serum it is necessary to know the type of pneumonia, and typing consumes critical time. Moreover the preparation of the serums is expensive, and the cost of treatment correspondingly high. A pharmaceutical that would be effective against the whole cocci family was sought, and partially found in a derivative of an unimportant dye intermediate. From this discovery evolved the *sulfa* drugs.

The fundamental intermediate is para benzene sulfonamide, $NH_2C_6H_4SO_2NH_2$, first modified by conversion to a magnesium salt, and rather ineffective. The intermediate itself, in highly purified form, was found to be quite good; but too many secondary reactions in the patient followed its use. Three thousand derivatives have been tested; but among them all only sulfapyridine, $NH_2C_6H_4SO_2NH·C_5H_4N$, sulfadiazine, $NH_2C_6H_4SO_2NH·C_4H_3N_2$, sulfathiazole, $NH_2C_6H_4SO_2NH·C_3H_2NS$, and sulfaguanidine, $NH_2C_6H_4SO_2NH·C(NH)NH_2·H_2O$, have met the exacting standards for this type of pharmaceutical. The sulfa drugs are produced by a series of chemical operations similar to those that produce dyes. The starting material is aniline. The apparatus is mostly glass-lined to insure maximum purity.

Sprays, ointments, and dusting powders containing the sulfa compounds are available for the treatment of open wounds and of burns.

The sulfa drugs stop the multiplication of the colonies of certain types of cocci which have gotten into the blood stream. Natural immunity then destroys the bacteria. These drugs, which must be administered under the close supervision of a skilled physician, act very quickly. For the several types of pneumonia there is no delay in treatment to await typing, as where serums are used.

The sulfa drugs are not effective against all the members of the cocci family of bacteria. For staphylococcus and other pus-forming organisms, *penicillin* has proven very effective. A selected strain of the common green mold found on bread and cheese, *penicillium notatum,* is grown under the most sterile conditions in large flat bottles or shallow tanks, in a broth containing starch or glucose for food, with small amounts of potash, phosphate, lime, and magnesia to promote vigorous growth. The living mold exudes a powerful bactericide in extremely minute quantity. The mold is discarded and penicillin is recovered from the broth.

Recovery of the minute quantities of the drug from the large volume of liquid is most difficult. The principle is to use a solvent for the penicillin which does not mix with water. In one process the solvent is amylacetate, which is agitated with the broth to extract a crude concentrate. Or a solution in ether is extracted with pure water, the new water solution with ether, and so on until a pure concentrated product is obtained. The penicillin is then dried at very low temperature.

As its chemical composition and its constitution have not yet been established, penicillin has not been synthesized.

Anesthetics. Ethyl ether, $(C_2H_5)_2O$, and chloroform, $CHCl_3$, are the two anesthetics in most general use; ethylene and cyclopropane are much less common. Certain compounds have local anesthetic action when they are applied to sensory nerve ends. Cocaine, $C_8H_{13}N(OOC_6H_5)(COOCH_3)$, extracted from coca leaves, was first used. It is habit-forming, and chemists labored long to find a synthetic substitute free from this fault. The first synthetic was Novocain, $NH_2C_6H_4COOCH_2CH_2N(C_2H_5)_2HCl$. It is made from aminobenzoic acid, ethyl alcohol, and hydrochloric acid. The aminobenzoic acid, as in cocaine, is the active agent and is modified by the ethyl group. Later products of this type contain methyl and propyl groups in place of the ethyl of the original synthetic product. In a very recent local anesthetic of the Novocain type, hydrobromic acid is found in place of hydrochloric.

Sedatives. These are the so-called sleeping powders. Chloral hydrate, $CCl_3CH(OH)_2$, often called chloral, was the first in general use, but has largely given place to the esters of barbituric acid, $NHCONHCOCH_2CO$. Veronal is the diethyl ester, $NHCONHCOC(C_2H_5)C$. Various proprietary modifications contain amyl, butyl, isopropyl groups in place of the ethyl units in the original synthetic, Veronal.

Analgesics. These compounds relieve pain and lower the temperature in fever. The base of a large number of proprietary drugs is salicylic acid, $C_6H_4OHCOOH$, which in tonnage is by far the most important of the coal-tar pharmaceuticals. Salicylic acid is made from phenol by first reacting with caustic soda, and then with dry carbon dioxide under pressure:

$$C_6H_5OH + NaOH = C_6H_5ONa + H_2O$$
$$C_6H_5ONa + CO_2 = C_6H_4OHCOONa$$

The sodium atom is then removed by treating with a strong acid such as sulphuric.

Salicylic acid has a powerful antiseptic action and is used in dusting powders. The sodium salt is used as a preservative for preventing fermentation. But of much greater importance is the derivative, Aspirin, acetosalicylic acid, $CH_3COOC_6H_4COOH$. This widely used analgesic is formed by reaction of the two acids, acetic and salicylic.

Other well known drugs for this purpose are acetanilide (Antifebrin), $CH_3CONHC_6H_5$, made from acetic acid and aniline; acetophenetidine, $C_2H_5OC_6H_4NHCOCH_3$, from ethyl alcohol, aniline, and acetic anhydride; antipyrine, $N(CH_3)N(C_6H_5)COCH:C(CH_3)$. There are many proprietary products on the market that contain one or another of these compounds.

Purgatives. Many of these are of natural origin. Castor oil, for example, is pressed from the castor bean. The extracts of aloe, cascara, sienna, rhubarb, all contain as the active principle a hydroxymethylanthraquinone. Many inorganic compounds have purgative action. Glauber salt, sodium sulphate, $Na_2SO_4 \cdot 10 \, H_2O$, is rather too active for human consumption, though it is used in large quantity in veterinary practice. Magnesium sulphate, Epsom salt, $MgSO_4 \cdot 7 \, H_2O$, is milder in action. Magnesium citrate, $Mg_3(C_6H_5O_7)_2 \cdot 14 \, H_2O$ is generally sold in solution in carbonated water.

A widely used synthetic purgative is phenol-phthalein, $C_{20}H_{14}O_4$. Phthalic anhydride, $C_6H_4(CO)_2O$, phenol, and sulphuric acid are heated together to form the compound. It is sold in tablets, in liquid, even in chewing gum.

Vitamins. The transformation of the carbohydrates (including starch and sugar) and of albuminous and protein compounds, together with fats and oils, produces tissue and supplies human energy requirements. The mineral salts required for bone and tissue building also come from these ordinary foods. But in addition to the above bulk materials a balanced diet for well-being and health must contain a dozen or more very complex organic compounds that belong to no single chemical class.

The essential character of these compounds (required only in very minute quantities) has been determined only by a process of elimination. Scurvy comes from a lack of fresh fruits and vegetables, and disappears when these foods are restored to the diet. Beriberi results from a diet chiefly of polished rice, yet is cured by the addition of the polishings to the rice diet. The first workers engaged in attempting to isolate the elusive compounds thought them to be amines, and called them "vital amines"—since contracted to "vitamins."

Because men and animals with a well balanced diet show none of the symptoms of vitamin deficiency, it has been necessary to study every food in order to detect all vitamins. This work is not yet completed; but the more important have been isolated, and some are now synthesized in chemical plants. This enables production on a large scale, and any deficiency in the natural diet may be compensated by supplementing the food, or giving direct dosage. The problems of synthesis have been numerous, for many of the products are extremely complicated in molecular structure, and this must be exactly duplicated in the factory product. A few important vitamins are:

Vitamin A. This increases resistance to infection through the skin and mucous membranes, promotes growth, aids night vision. It is found in green and yellow vegetables, and in the oils extracted from the livers of several varieties of fish. Vitamin A is an alcohol of formula $C_{20}H_{29}OH$, and occurs in fish oil as an ester. The fatty acids of the fish oil are converted to soap, and the vitamin concentrates in the residue.

Vitamin B complex. Originally called vitamin B, this has been found to contain at least a half-dozen well defined compounds, and probably more that are not yet identified. The vitamin B group will cure beriberi and certain nerve disorders. It is extracted from animal livers. The several components are:

Vitamin B_1, thiamin chloride, $C_{12}H_{17}ON_4SCl \cdot HCl$. It was long extracted from the polishings of rice, but now is made synthetically. The process involves a long series of reactions, starting with ethyl formate, ethyl ethoxypropionate, and acetamide. It is necessary to metabolism.

Vitamin B_2, riboflavin, $C_{17}H_{20}N_4O_6$. This is the growth promoting vitamin. It is of great assistance in curing pellagra, possibly also beriberi. It is produced synthetically in large quantities, though the process is quite complicated.

Vitamins B_3, B_4, B_5. These are present in the vitamin B complex, but little is known as to their chemical composition or specific clinical action.

Vitamin B_6, pyridoxine hydrochloride, $C_8H_{11}O_3N \cdot HCl$. It assists in the cure of pellagra. It may be made synthetically.

Among the constituents of the B complex is pantothenic acid, $HOCH_2C(CH_3)_2CHOHCONHCH_2CH_2COOH$. It is complementary to vitamin B_2 in the cure of pellagra, and seems necessary to cell growth.

Vitamin C, ascorbic acid, $C_6H_8O_6$. This occurs in citrus fruits. It is both preventive and cure for scurvy, and exerts an important influence on the healthy structure of bones and teeth. It is produced in large amounts by the fermentation of sorbitol, which is made from glucose.

Vitamin D. This is a derivative of ergosterine, $C_{27}H_{42}OH$, and is probably a complex of several similar compounds. It prevents and cures rickets, promoting the absorption of calcium and phosphorus. Exposure of the body or of foods to ultraviolet light increases the vitamin D content. It is derived from fish oils in concentrated form, and has not been synthesized.

Vitamin E, alpha tocopherol, $C_{29}H_{50}O_2$. This is an alcohol found in the oil of the wheat germ. While it has been synthesized, oil extracted from the wheat germ has supplied the small quantities required in America. Its absence causes sterility in both man and animals.

Vitamin H, biotin, $C_{10}H_{16}O_3N_2S$. This is sometimes called the supervitamin, since it promotes the growth of yeast, which is particularly rich in the B vitamins. Biotin makes the skin resistant to dermatitis. It has been synthesized in the laboratory.

Vitamin K. There are several forms of this vitamin, and they all contain a naphthoquinone nucleus which assists in the clotting of blood. It is extracted from alfalfa meal.

Vitamin P, eriodictine, $C_{15}H_{11}O_6$. This prevents capillary bleeding. It is extracted from citrus and paprika juices.

Vitamin PP, nicotinic acid, C_5H_4NCOOH. This prevents and cures pellagra. It may be made from nicotine extracted from tobacco, by simple oxidation. Since large quantities are required in the treatment of white flour, a more abundant material, pyridine, found in coal tar, is now the starting raw material for industrial production. A derivative, nicotinamide, $C_5H_4N \cdot NH_2$, is often used in place of the nicotinic acid.

Hormones. Animals have several glands, some of them ductless, that secrete minute quantities of complex chemical compounds carried by the blood stream to organs, which they excite into activity. In a manner these compounds may be compared to catalysts. Apparently the same materials are common to all warm-blooded animals; and where the chemist has been unable to synthesize the compounds he extracts them from similar glands obtained from the slaughterhouse, or from animal secretions.

For the metabolism of carbohydrates, the hormone *insulin* is necessary. If derangement of its natural source, the pancreas, causes a deficiency, diabetes follows. To make up the deficiency, insulin may be extracted from the pancreas of an animal and injected subcutaneously into the sufferer. Because of the prevalence of diabetes, the production of insulin has become an important industry.

Fresh pancreatic glands of hogs and cattle are frozen solid, ground fine, and extracted with a 3 per cent solution of hydrochloric acid in ethyl alcohol. This solution is separated from the ground pulp, concentrated by boiling—in a very high vacuum in order to keep the temperature as low as possible—and the concentrate is diluted with strong alcohol and left to stand for some hours, in order to precipitate out unwanted portions. The operation is repeated several times. Finally a crude insulin is crystallized out and refined to the pharmaceutical grade.

Adrenalin, methylaminoethanolcatechol, with the chemical formula $(OH)_2C_6H_3CHOHCH_2NHCH_3$, may be made synthetically, but is actually extracted from the adrenal glands of cattle. It exerts a very powerful constriction on the blood vessels.

Thyroxin, tetraiodophenyl-oxytyrosine, which has the formula $HOC_6H_2I_2OC_6H_2I_2CH_2CHNH_2COOH$, may be made synthetically; but most of the commercial product is extracted from thyroid glands of cattle. It increases greatly the metabolism of body-stored sugars, and is used in treating obesity.

There are a number of important sex hormones—for example, estrone, progesterone—of which ergosterol, $C_{27}H_{42}O$, forms the nucleus. They have not been made synthetically; but, because of their very valuable medicinal effects and the great difficulty in collecting sufficient raw materials for production on any scale, a large amount of research is going on.

Although remarkable progress has been made, synthetic pharmaceutical chemistry is really only in its infancy. The chemist is learning the clinical value of the many organic groups, and one of these days most of the serious diseases will yield to his synthetic products. Research work in the field requires infinite patience, for the compounds suspected to have therapeutic value must first be most carefully purified, then tried for efficiency and tolerance on test animals. Finally, if the results appear satisfactory, the new product is passed over to the physician for trial in the clinic. Often years are required before a new product can be marketed.

Chapter XVII

COSMETICS, TOILETRIES, PERFUMES

The number and variety of these products is almost beyond belief. A billion dollars' worth are sold annually. If all the servicing is included, they make up one of the country's large industries, and hence a very important market for the manufacturer of organic chemical products.

Cosmetics and perfumes are merely blends or mixtures involving little chemistry. But they come in contact with human skin, and all skins do not react alike to chemicals. An abnormal skin reaction is called *allergy,* and a long list of products likely to cause skin trouble has been compiled from experience. Such a list is the fundamental text of the cosmetic and perfume industries. But in spite of the greatest care in selecting the safest known ingredients, there is always an odd individual with an unusual allergic tendency. A change of the brand of powder or lipstick is frequently all that is necessary to take care of such cases.

Cosmetics are marketed in the form of paste, cream, powder, and liquid. In commercial importance the soaps rank first, the dentifrices next, and then the creams and powders. Perfumes are important; but they and their cousins—the essential oils forming the flavoring materials—are also incorporated in the various cosmetics and toiletries, and it is difficult to rank them in the over-all picture.

Dentifrices are produced in three forms: powder, paste, and liquid. The powders contain an abrasive material, a soap, and a flavor. The abrasive should be very soft, the commonest being a pure precipitated chalk, a form of calcium carbonate, $CaCO_3$. Natural chalk is usually too impure, and is rarely used in tooth powders. Tricalcium phosphate, $Ca_3P_2O_8$, precipitated from phosphoric acid and milk of lime under carefully controlled conditions, does not scratch tooth enamel, and takes the place of chalk in some cases.

Powdered white Castile soap, once made only from olive oil and caustic soda, is the preferred soap base; but soaps made from almost any good vegetable oil are used. The function of the soap is to remove the thickened mucus from the teeth and gums. The flavoring material, principally for disguising the soap, is one of the natural essential oils: peppermint, spearmint, or wintergreen.

The pastes are essentially like the powders. Their soft consistency is due to admixture of alcohol and glycerine. Chemical bleaching agents such as sodium perborate, $NaBO_3 \cdot 4\,H_2O$, potassium chlorate, $KClO_3$, or potassium iodate, KIO_3, are sometimes added in very small amounts. These bleach out the yellow organic coloring matter that tends to coat teeth.

Liquid dentifrices are relatively new products and contain such chemical detergents as are described on page 125. They are really dentifrices, and must not be confused with mouth washes, which are primarily intended for sterilizing and have little cleansing power.

Mouth washes contain a mild disinfectant—such as thymol, $CH_3(C_3H_7)C_6H_3OH$, or menthol, $C_{10}H_{19}OH$ (both from essential oils)—and less frequently very dilute phenol disguised by an added flavor. Alcohol and glycerine are found in some of them, as well as artificial coloring of a harmless nature.

Depilatories depend for their action on a soluble sulphide, such as barium sulphide, BaS, calcium sulphide, CaS, or strontium sulphide, SrS. Sodium sulphide has more active dissolving action on hair, but it is too caustic for the average skin. The same is true of arsenic sulphide, As_2S_3. For cosmetic purposes the pure sulphides are diluted with starch or talc; but even when diluted they should be used with great caution.

Complexion creams are of very varied composition, indeed. The common base is a vegetable oil, mixed with a wax or a grease, and the whole is emulsified into a creamy product with alcohol, glycerine, sometimes water. The better grades use almond oil and lanolin for the oil and grease portion; the cheaper, cottonseed or coconut oil and a soft paraffine. An antiseptic is added, both as germicide, and for preservative effect on the creams containing the cheaper oils. Zinc stearate, $Zn(C_{18}H_{35}O_2)_2$, borax, $Na_2B_4O_7 \cdot 10\ H_2O$, or benzoate of soda, $NaC_7H_5O_2$, serves this double function. The astringent creams contain alums. Almost all are perfumed.

Face powders are built around a base, preferably of starch, some- times of talcum. Rice flour is the best form of starch, because per- spiration makes it only slightly sticky. Corn and wheat starches are used in the cheaper powders. Talcum, a ground mineral (silicate of magnesium) is used in toilet powders. The powder bases are ground to extreme fineness and are bolted, or sized in an air blast, to remove any coarse particles. Color is added in the grinding. Rouge is a powder colored by oxide of iron, Fe_2O_3, a harmless coloring agent. The addition of stearic acid, or of zinc stearate, increases the adherence to the skin; and the latter has a mild antiseptic action. The powders are usually perfumed.

Grease paints are compounded of soft waxes (the lipstick is a special form). They consist of a mixture of soft and hard waxes, and an oil-soluble color. The hard wax is a paraffine, or blend of paraf- fine and beeswax. The soft wax is vaseline, a soft paraffine. A "kiss- proof" variety contains carnauba wax or, even better, ceresin.

Nail polishes are of two kinds: one is an ordinary polishing powder, formulated much like a tooth powder; the other is a true lacquer. The latter consists of nitrocellulose dissolved in a suitable solvent, usually amyl acetate, $CH_3COOCH_2CH_2CH_2CH_2CH_3$. Be- cause of its characteristic odor this solvent is often called banana oil. The color is a pigment. Polish remover is just the solvent.

The selection of colors for tinting the powders, rouges, and nail polishes is an art, for light varies widely in quality. Most electric lamps give off a light much richer in yellows and oranges than sun- light, and the same reddish shades will appear quite different under the two sources of light. The better cosmetics for use under arti- ficial lighting differ from the day powders, allowing for the differ- ence in illumination, and should not be used at the wrong hour nor in places for which they were not designed.

Cosmetics for the stage vary in coloring from those for the street and the drawing room. Photographic film differs from the eye in color sensitivity, and so special cosmetics are necessary for the movie star.

Shaving soaps, like toilet soaps, contain much more fatty acid or oil than that saponified by the alkali. Their hardness and firm texture are due to the caustic soda used in their preparation.

Shaving creams are of two kinds. The ordinary lathering type has a formula similar to that of a shaving soap, but with caustic potash and an excess of oil. They are made into paste with glycerine, which retards the drying of the lather. The brushless creams use an organic alkali, triethanolamine, $N(CH_2CH_2OH)_3$, to saponify the fatty acid into a soft soap, in which it also emulsifies a large excess of the oil.

Perfumes are as old as history.

The pleasant odors of many flowers are due to their characteristic essential oils. These may be in the flower, the leaf, or even in the woody stock. In the flower they are most abundant just before maturity, after which they are absorbed into the plant and transformed into other compounds. Chemically most of the oils belong to the aromatic series of hydrocarbon derivatives, for they are esters, aldehydes, and ketones. They are quite volatile at low temperatures, and it is in vapor form that they are carried to the nostrils.

The method of extracting the essential oil from a flower depends on the character of the oil. The most delicate and prized odors are in compounds so very easily decomposed that a mechanical rather than a chemical process must be used if their full value is to be preserved for the perfumer. A layer of fat—one that is insoluble in alcohol—is placed on the bottom of a shallow tray or on a glass plate, and freshly picked flowers are pressed into it. The fat absorbs the odor from the blossoms, which are then removed and replaced by a fresh lot. This is repeated until the fat becomes saturated. The essential oils are all soluble in alcohol, and are extracted from the fat in a highly concentrated alcohol solution. The fat is used several times, but finally becomes rancid and is disposed of to the soapmaker.

Cheaper oils are extracted from the flowers by a very volatile solvent, such as ether, chloroform, or carbon tetrachloride. The solvent is then evaporated under vacuum at a very low temperature, leaving a concentrated residue of the oil and any other dissolved material. This method has been improved, to yield a higher-grade oil, by adding a wax to the solution before evaporation. The wax holds the essential oil, which can be extracted from it by alcohol, eliminating some of the undesired impurities.

Some oils are so stable that they can be steamed out of the flower. The blooms are placed on racks, and steam is blown through, and condensed. The resulting oil-water mixture is allowed to settle, and the oil floats on top. The oils distilled by steam are usually only a part of the odor-producing compounds in the bloom, and are much inferior to those extracted with fat.

The aromatic series of organic compounds is so named because many of them have a marked odor (only a few would be classed as perfumes). It is possible to prepare synthetics that have odors resembling those of natural flowers. For example, benzyl acetate, $C_6H_5CH_2COOCH_3$, has an odor resembling that of the natural oil of jasmine. It is prepared in a simple, though indirect, way from toluene and acetic acid. The natural oils are complex blends of many components, and therefore the matching with synthetics is never perfect. A skillful perfumer, however, can compound a number of synthetics so as to arrive at a sufficiently close approximation for the cheaper perfumes.

The compounding of a perfume in the form found on the dressing table is a fine art acquired only with long experience. Perfumes must be non-allergic, and must not stain, bleach or dissolve fabrics. They must evaporate as a unit and leave no ill-smelling residue. The odors of the concentrated essential oils are much too intense for use in the raw state. Only a specially purified ethyl alcohol may be used as an extending medium in the better grade of perfumes.

The perfumer retards the rate of evaporation of the oil with a "fixative"—ambergris, a waxy material from the sperm whale, for the highest-grade perfumes. But ambergris is very scarce and expensive, and various natural gums and balsams also are used. Recently synthetic products—such as esters of benzyl alcohol, C_6H_5OH —have been used successfully.

Very large quantities of perfume materials are used in soaps and in the common cosmetics. Fly sprays, floor waxes, polishes, and many household supplies are now perfumed, often to disguise unattractive odors inherent in their ingredients. Wearing apparel is perfumed to eliminate the odor of the finishing mill. These industrial perfumes are made of synthetic materials, for subtlety is not important. For soap, synthetic oil of almonds, benzaldehyde, C_6H_5CHO, is used. A similar odor is imparted by oil of Niobe, methyl benzoate, $CH_3OOCC_6H_5$. Orange blossom is closely matched by methyl anthranilate, $CH_3NHC_6H_4COOCH_3$; clover blossom, by methyl acetophenone, $CH_3COC_6H_4CH_3$. Synthetic oil of wintergreen is methyl salicylate, $HOC_6H_4COOCH_3$.

Most cosmetics and perfumes are proprietary articles, and each manufacturer has his own formulations. It would be impossible to discuss or even list them all, and only typical products have been described. The larger manufacturers maintain excellent research laboratories, and follow every new development of the chemical industry eagerly for possible application in their field. The modern cosmetic plants are marvels of chemical engineering, and place great emphasis on the quality of the product.

CHAPTER XVIII

COLLOIDS

It is a common saying that oil and water do not mix. But with proper agitating equipment it is possible to produce a rather good mixture of kerosene and water; as soon as the agitator is stopped the mixture again tends to separate. A little soap added during the agitation will produce an emulsion of the oil in the water that will remain stable for a long time.

The cook takes olive oil, vinegar (a dilute solution of acetic acid), and egg yolk and beats them into a stiff mayonnaise. Properly made, this remains a stiff paste for a long time. Without the egg, the mixture will separate.

In California some oil wells deliver a particularly viscous oil containing as much as 40 per cent salt water. This refuses to separate, however long it is stored in tanks, yet the oil sent to the refinery must be free from water and salt. The petroleum industry spends a large sum of money each year in breaking these oil emulsions.

A long list of similar examples could be compiled, many of them intimately related to our daily lives. Some common desserts, jellies, pastes, sauces, paints, varnishes, lacquers, cosmetics, many of the life processes, fall into this group. The underlying phenomenon is not easy to identify, and some very puzzling problems confront the worker in this field.

Many years ago it was recognized that the emulsion of oil, water, and soap behaved quite differently from a solution of a salt in water. A new branch of the science grew from this observation. It is named *colloidal chemistry,* from the Greek word kolla (glue), for glue is a very characteristic colloid. Actually it is questionable if this is a branch of chemistry, dealing as it does with a form or state of matter rather than with a composition or chemical change.

Most of the phenomena and the manipulations belong rather to the realm of physics.

In order to understand a colloid and why it behaves differently from the usual crystalline materials, some concept of magnitudes is necessary. The metric system of measurement is used in scientific work, the metric unit of length being the meter, approximately equivalent to 40 inches. The meter is divided into a thousand parts, called millimeters, one of which equals approximately 0.04 inch. In turn the millimeter is divided into a thousand microns; that is, one micron (μ) is about 0.00004 inch. The micron in turn is divided into a thousand millimicrons; that is, each millimicron ($\mu\mu$) is about four hundred-millionths of an inch. The smallest particle that can be seen by our best optical microscopes has a diameter of about a hundred millimicrons.

Assume a cube of gold 10 millimeters on an edge; its surface will be 600 square millimeters (six faces, each 100 square millimeters in area). Now slice this cube into smaller cubes, each 1 millimeter on an edge, making 1,000 of these smaller units. Their combined surface area will be 6,000 square millimeters. This act of subdivision has multiplied the superficial area of the original gold ten times. Again slice the smaller particles in the same manner by cutting at tenths on each edge. Each small cube will be cut into 1,000 smaller ones, and one now has a million of the smaller cubes, with a total superficial area of 60,000 square millimeters. If thrown into water, they will sink to the bottom as a yellow powder. Keep repeating this operation until the individual cube is only 1 millimicron on an edge. There will be a sextillion of these small cubes, with a surface area of six quadrillion square millimeters. If this very fine powder is thrown into water it will not sink, but will disperse throughout the liquid, and give it a brilliant red color.

No particles are visible in the solution, even in a powerful microscope, for each is smaller than the limit of visibility. It is possible to prove that there are actual gold particles floating in the liquid by the use of a very simple principle. A ray of sunlight crossing a dark room is made easily visible by stirring up dust, the light

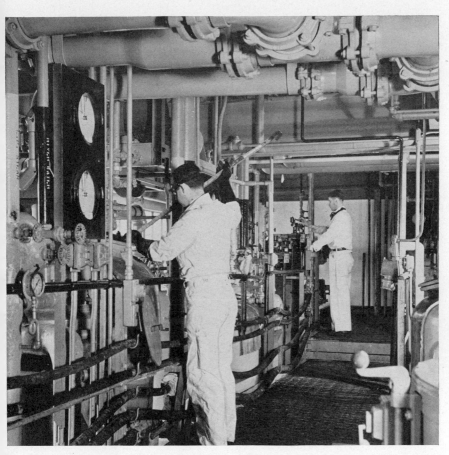

A MODERN PHARMACEUTICAL UNIT

THE RESEARCH LABORATORY, 1942

Preparing a new organic chemical

reflected from the dust particles in the beam marking the outline of the ray quite distinctly. If a ray of light of great intensity is projected into the red solution, and one views, across the beam, he will see a yellow reflection, from the particles of gold.

If the gold is still further reduced in size, the red color is no longer produced, and the solution takes on a yellow color; for the gold particles are now approaching the size of the individual molecule, and the liquid is taking on the characteristic of a true solution.

The red solution of the gold is said to be a colloidal solution; the gold present is in the colloid state. Actually it can be made quite simply. A dilute solution of gold chloride in water may be precipitated by an organic reducing agent in the form or metallic gold in such fine state of division that it will be in colloidal form. Or an electric arc may be sprung between two gold electrodes under the surface of water, and the red solution will result. In this case the electric arc vaporizes the gold, and the vapor is condensed in very small particles.

The colloidal state is therefore characterized by an extremely fine state of subdivision, yet is above the dimension of the simple molecule. Polymers and molecules of very complex compounds may be large enough to be in this state. The great size of the superficial area as compared to the mass accounts for the peculiar behavior.

The colloidal particles take an electric charge, plus or minus, depending on the substance. A few may take a charge of either sign. The charge of a particle resides on its surface; the surface of the particle is large in comparison to its mass, and the amount of charge is correspondingly great. It is the electric charge of the particle that accounts for much of its peculiar behavior.

Consider again the making of mayonnaise. The mixing operation breaks up the oil particles into minute globules, which are surrounded by watery vinegar. The egg yolk consists of complex organic compounds in a colloidal state. The dispersed colloids surround the oil globules with a sort of skin kept in place by electric forces, and resist displacement. This holds apart adjacent oil globules, and prevents any tendency to coalesce. Thus the colloid "stabilizes" the emulsion. The same is true of the soap in the kerosene-water emulsion. In the California oil, an asphaltum compound collects in the interface between the oil and the brine.

Emulsions can be broken in many ways. Heating may destroy the colloid, and some California oil emulsions are broken by heating to a high temperature. Since the basis is electric charge, some emulsions may be broken by sending the oil over charged electrodes, which neutralize the charge on the colloid. A chemical reagent having an opposite charge may be added for the same purpose.

The stability of an emulsion is often increased by adding a colloid of suitable character to the dispersed mixture. For example, jelly is a mixture of a fruit juice, an organic acid, sugar, etc., cooked together in a large quantity of water. To insure a firm, stable jelly a colloid, pectin, must be added. This is found in quantity in apples and some other fruits and is now extracted and prepared in concentrated form for direct addition to fruit juices that are difficult to jell.

Soap is effective because it is a colloid that aids in emulsifying the oil that makes the dirt adhere so firmly.

Fog is composed of minute particles of water dispersed in air. The water particles have electric charges, and a coating of smoke and dust, both facts interfering with coalescence. If electrically charged sand is sprinkled through the fog, the charges on the water are neutralized, the particles coalesce, and drop as mist.

In a true solution—of a crystalline salt in water, for example— the dispersed molecules of the solute are very much smaller than colloidal particles. Many sera contain protein compounds of characteristic colloidal nature. It is possible to separate the dissolved compounds from the colloids by a peculiar type of filtration called *dialysis*. Materials like animal gut, parchment, even cellophane, have pores fine enough to retain the colloid and yet pass the dissolved salt. The material to be refined is suspended in a bag made of one of these membranes, and suspended in a tank of running water. The dissolved salt will pass through the membrane, leaving the colloidal material behind.

Most catalysts—particularly those used for accelerating reactions between gases—have a very porous structure. Which is another way of saying they have enormous surface. In this respect their state resembles the colloidal, even though they are not in a dispersed condition. Some catalysts are actually prepared from bases in colloidal form; for example, the silica-alumina catalyst used in the catalytic cracking of petroleum.

The colloidal state plays a most important part in modern technology. Only a very few examples are within the scope of this book. It is a relatively young branch of science, and has much ahead of it.

CHAPTER XIX

CHEMICAL RESEARCH

Several hundred years ago an Englishman opposed the idea that all material things were constituted of air, fire, earth, and water, for he had found in his laboratory some twenty-odd elemental substances that could not be broken down into simpler products. This research resulted in the atomic theory.

From time immemorial, smallpox was a most dreaded scourge, for which there seemed to be no assured remedy. A hundred and fifty years ago, a physician noticed that a person surviving an attack had an immunity against reinfection. He noticed that infection of the less virulent cowpox seemed to give immunity to smallpox. All observations confirmed this concept, and led to the experiment of inoculating with cowpox, the first vaccine.

A chemist, disappointed with the irregular quality of the imported natural indigo, made a thorough study of its constitution, determined the active ingredient, and set about producing it synthetically. Synthetic indigo is a result of this research.

Today three hundred million dollars is spent annually in the United States to find out things not previously known. Scientific research is a highly organized activity, and is fostered by the federal, state, and local subdivisions of government, by colleges and universities, by privately endowed institutions, and by industrial corporations and trade associations. Tens of thousands of highly trained workers devote their lives to wresting from Nature the secrets that will lead to new materials, and to finding new applications for available products. These workers are picked for their intelligence, their advanced education, their inquiring minds. Their labors are highly systematized, and in consequence their production is enormous.

All discoveries were once the result of accident. There was no specific aim, no organized program of work, no goal towards which work was directed. Later, a haphazard, hit-or-miss method of trying anything produced valuable but infrequent results. Finally, scientific method and planned research became almost universal.

The staff of a research institution is its most valuable asset. The members must be highly trained in the fundamentals of that branch of science in which they are working. The faculties of our colleges and universities have a profound scientific background, and each year, in addition to training the young, make outstanding contributions to general knowledge. Libraries contain the accumulated store of recorded experience, and are the first tool used in any research problem. In the library, the researcher can learn what has already been done on the particular problem confronting him. The solution is not in any library, but a study of earlier attempts eliminates the necessity of starting at the beginning. Moreover, discussion of a somewhat parallel or analogous situation may provide a valuable hint and lead to a train of thought or to an experiment that will carry the experimenter a long way towards his obscure goal.

The simplest research problem is to duplicate the composition of some commercial product, or to find a substitute with like properties. The solution may be found in a library (a vast amount of chemical information has been well indexed and classified). Or perhaps it will follow an analysis—which may entail a routine chemical procedure, or may draw upon the assistance of the crystallographer and the physicist. Then follows the preparation of small trial lots in the glassware of the laboratory. Finally the whole has to be transferred to an assembled pilot plant, where the engineering data are obtained for the building of a production unit.

A more complex type of research problem would be the development of a new plastic for a special purpose not served by any available material. An experienced plastic chemist familiar with the whole field would study the new specifications and compare them, item for item, with the properties of the most likely existing plastics, in the hope that these, by modification, could be made to serve. The modification might include changes in formula, in the filler, or in the molding cycle—all of which would necessitate preparation of working batches and the molding of test pieces.

If this method of attack should fail, the plastic chemist would survey all the raw materials which, experience indicated, might be components of a plastic that would meet the specified requirements. Then he would learn how to bring about reactions between these materials, and how to make a molding compound. The task might mean years of patient and trying experimentation. It took ten years and more than a hundred chemists and engineers to perfect Nylon as a textile yarn.

Behind this applied research there is another kind of scientific inquiry called pure, or fundamental, research. Its results have no immediate commercial application, and production is not an incentive. It is devoted solely to increasing general knowledge—for example, of the fundamental properties of materials, of the course of chemical reactions, of the production of new compounds. All such research is primary, and the stock of fundamental knowledge thus accumulated is drawn upon for applied research.

The research laboratories of the chemical industry are not wholly devoted to purely chemical work. Many chemical phenomena are only manifested through physical changes, and a surprising amount of chemical knowledge is derived from methods and manipulations belonging to the realm of physics. The phenomena of light, heat, electricity greatly affect and frequently shorten the work of the chemist. Many physical tests are required to prove whether new products of the chemical industry are fit for commercial applications.

The preliminary experiments in a laboratory are carried on with small quantities in glass equipment. Glass is very resistant to the attacks of the several chemical reagents, and lets the chemist see what is going on.

Once a procedure for making a new product has been established, the chemical engineer takes over. He studies each manufacturing step in detail, and designs and constructs a miniature plant, using small commercial apparatus of which he has a stock at hand. A limited production is undertaken, corrections are made, and finally the plans for a huge industrial plant are drawn.

There is no magic in industrial chemistry. A magician can wave his wand over his hat for a long time without the emergence of any new plastic, pharmaceutical, or synthetic textile. Only hard, patient, and intelligently directed work produces such miracles. There is no mystery: Nature gives us certain raw materials, the scientist applies his knowledge, the technician gives his procedural techniques, and humanity receives a better standard of living.

The molecule has become your servant.

NOMENCLATURE

The nomenclature, or jargon, of the chemist is puzzling to the uninitiated, and rightly so because it does not conform to any unified system. The manufacturing operations may be readily broken down into a limited number of "unit processes," many of them in common use in one or another form, the chemical engineer selecting for his purpose the most efficient type for the problem at hand. These units are then arranged in proper sequence to facilitate the flow of materials through the operation. A few of the more important unit processes are the following:

Crushing and grinding. Most chemical operations convert raw materials, usually natural minerals, and require that these be broken down to smaller sizes to facilitate reaction. Machines which break largely by pressure are called crushers; by a blow, disintegrators; by abrasion, pulverizers or grinding mills.

Crushers are built to take a block as big as six feet and crack it into smaller pieces. They are operated in series for reduction to the smallest sizes, the limit in smallness being a quarter- to half-inch diameter.

Disintegrators are used to reduce brittle and preferably rather soft materials to fine powders. They are usually fed with matter that has passed through crushers and is less than an inch in size, although some of the most modern operate efficiently on larger lumps.

Pulverizers and mills are designed for grinding materials to fine powder—for example, Portland cement. They work usually on a crusher product less than an inch in size; what they put out may be as fine as two-thousandths of an inch—even finer, at great reduction in their hourly capacity. A crude type of such apparatus is the stone mill of the flour mill: A gritty circular sandstone is fixed in the bed of the machine; above is suspended on an adjustable support, so that it can be rotated, a similar circular stone. The grain is fed through the center of the top stone and is rubbed fine as it passes out between the stones to be discharged at the circumference.

For large-scale grinding the tube mill is in general use. This is a horizontal cylindrical shell lined with a wear-resistant material, and suspended in trunnions so it can be rotated about its axis. It is loaded with small pebbles or steel balls, which roll as the mill is rotated. The feed is introduced through one trunnion, the finished product discharged through the other. The material fed to the mill, either wet or dry, is broken down between the rolling balls, or against the lining.

The *sizing* of broken materials is accomplished in several ways. Relatively coarse products such as lump ore are passed over a grizzly: an inclined series of spaced bars, the distance between the individual members being suited to the size of product to be separated. The crushed ore slides down the grizzly, the fine pieces falling between the bars. The coarse material slides over the end and may be returned to the crushing unit for further reduction.

Finer materials are sized on a screen of wire mesh or perforated plate. Wire cloth is made for sizing purposes with openings as large as an inch, and as small as two-thousandths of an inch. Wire-mesh screens are usually designated by the number of openings per linear inch—mesh, as it is called. The size of the openings depends on the diameter of the wire used in weaving the cloth; screens of 100-mesh (opening about six-thousandths of an inch) are the practicable limit in commercial sizing. Where the abrasion of the wire is likely to contaminate the product, bolting cloth is used; this is made of a hard twilled textile thread.

For fine screens the product must either be absolutely dry, or else be carried in suspension in a liquid. With fine-mesh screens, sizing is very slow unless the screen is shaken by mechanical means, or vibrated by electromagnets. For very fine materials there are better methods than screening.

It is well known that a current of air will pick up dust and carry it along, dropping it as the velocity of the current decreases. This principle is put to use in the air separator, for the sizing of finely ground materials: As the powder is fed into the separator it is picked up by a blast of air, the velocity of which is then reduced, so that it drops out the coarser particles first, and then successively finer and finer ones. Thus a separation into the desired grades may easily be made by inserting a dividing plate.

The same principle may be applied to fine materials suspended in a liquid medium; and devices that work on these are called hydroseparators. They are in many forms, the simplest of which is a hollow inverted cone: A stream of water enters the cone at the apex, its velocity lessening as it rises towards the base. The liquid carrying the solids is fed through a pipe opening near the apex. The rising current picks up the solid lifting it until the velocity is insufficient to carry it farther. The cone is so dimensioned that the overflow from the top rim carries out the material of the desired fineness. Another opening in the lower part of the cone carries off the oversize.

A very common problem is the separation of solids from liquids. If these are coarse a wire screen will separate them as the liquid drains through. For fine materials it is not satisfactory as the screen becomes blocked and holds back the liquid.

Liquids may be pressed from solids, as in the common cider press. Here the crushed apple is packed in a stout cloth and squeezed between the platens of a heavy press, the cider running through the mesh of the cloth and the pomace remaining behind. Oils are pressed from oil seeds by the same method. It is most effective where there is a relatively small amount of liquid in comparison to the volume of the solid.

Sedimentation. Differences in specific gravity of solids and liquids may be used to bring about separation. If the solid is lighter than the liquid it moves towards the top of a quiescent mixture; if heavier, it sinks. Mechanical equipment is available to skim off floating material or to remove settled mud, so that this principle may be applied to a continuously operating separation.

Filtration. There are several modifications of the principle in general use in the chemical industry. The simplest of all is the system used for treating our city water supplies: A support, usually of concrete, is covered with a thick layer of coarse gravel or crushed stone, and over this are finer and finer layers, the topmost of which is clean washed sand. The water to be clarified is distributed over the sand bed and seeps through, leaving the solid matter behind. From time to time the filter bed must be cleaned by scraping off the accumulated solids, and passing water back up through the bed. This system is used only where the quantity of solids to be removed is small in relation to the volume of liquid, and where the solids have no value (for they become contaminated by particles of sand).

The most common solid-liquid separator in chemical plants is the plate and frame filter press. To retain the solids, this uses a fine-textured cloth, of cotton, wool, asbestos, cabled wire, or a synthetic fiber, the choice being dependent on resistance to the chemical action of the materials under treatment. The press itself consists of alternate solid plates and hollow frames, both usually of rectangular cross-section. Side lugs permit these to slide on heavy horizontal parallel rails which are fastened to end pieces that support them at a suitable distance above the floor.

The plates and frames are accurately machined to a true surface around their edges, so that when brought together with a cloth between they are liquid-tight, even under high pressure. The central area of the plates is recessed slightly and cut with vertical grooves, or in another pattern, so that the cloth does not lie against a solid smooth surface. The frames are hollow chambers of a thickness varying from a fraction of an inch to several inches, the choice depending on the character of the solids to be separated.

Several registering holes are cut through the rims of the frames and the plates, one such connecting only with the interior of the frames to supply the feed to all simultaneously. The grooves on the faces of the plates all lead to a channel at the bottom which in turn connects with a passage to the outside where it is closed with an individual spigot on the plate.

A filter cloth is folded over the frame so as to cover both sides, forming a closed filter cell with cloth sides. The liquid to be filtered is forced by a pump in the appropriate channel and thence into the filter cells. The press is set up with plates and frames alternating, the frames covered by the cloth. With a screw or hydraulic plunger, the whole is then squeezed together so that it is liquid-tight under pressure. All the spigots are opened, and the pump is started. Under the pressure of the pump the cells are filled and the liquid forced out through the cloth, the solid remaining in the cell. Should a cloth break, only the spigot running cloudy need be shut off; the rest of the press can remain in operation. Large units with hundreds of square feet of filter area occupy little floor space.

When the press is filled, so that it delivers no more liquid, the liquors may be washed from the solid cakes if it has been provided with wash channels. It is then opened and the cakes are dumped, by tipping the frames hanging on the side rods. The cloths are scraped, and the whole equipment again assembled. A modified form of press may even be cleaned without opening; this is used where the cake is of no value.

The filter wheel is a continuously operating device in which the cloth is fixed to the surface of a revolting drum. This dips into the liquid to be separated, and vacuum is applied to the submerged section, sucking the liquid into the interior and leaving the cake on the surface of the cloth. As the wheel revolves, a knife scrapes the cake off. If the wheel is built in sections, and each section is connected with a rotary valve on the axle, the strong liquid and separate washes may be recovered.

The centrifuge is another favored method of separating liquids from solids where these are not too fine or slimy. It consists of a circular basket suspended on a vertical shaft so that the whole may be rotated at a very high speed. The basket is perforated, and is lined with a cloth of fabric or wire mesh. The basket is turned over slowly and the feed run in, the centrifugal force throwing it against the screen on the side of the basket. The liquid is forced out through the mesh, building up a cake. Then full speed is applied to expel the maximum of liquid. A wash may be given by spraying in water. When all the liquid possible is extracted, the basket is stopped, and the operator breaks down the cake, which may be discharged through a gate in the bottom. The machine can be discharged with a mechanical cutter, even made continuous in operation.

This same principle may be applied to separate two liquids which do not mix, if they have different specific gravities. The heavier will move to the circumference of the bowl, the lighter towards the axis, separate skimming devices being used for removal. The ordinary cream separator is such a device.

Distillation. Mixed liquids which have different boiling temperatures may be separated by distillation. The liquid with the lower boiling point will evaporate first, and may be condensed and collected. Where the boiling points are close together, this does not always yield pure products, and it may be necessary to repeat the process a number of times for complete separation. Equivalent results, without duplication of effort, may be obtained by setting on the boiling kettle a still head, or rectifying column.

The usual form of the rectifying column is a vertical cylindrical shell divided into sections by horizontal plates. The plates are perforated, and each perforation has a short upward-extending tube. The tube has a cap, somewhat larger in diameter than itself, with a skirt reaching a short distance down the tube. Each plate can collect and hold a thin layer of liquid equal in depth to the height of the tube, and the cap extends just below the surface of the liquid.

In operation a stream of the first distillate is fed into the column somewhere near the top plates, overflows the tubes, and runs down to the next below, and so on. The vapors from the boiling kettle pass upward through the perforations of the plates, being forced by the bubblecaps to bubble through the liquid on each plate. The plates thus become reboilers, condensing the vapor of the liquid of higher boiling point and evaporating the liquid of lower boiling point, and thus bringing about a redistillation that may be repeated as many times as there are plates in the column; in consequence, the vapors passing out are rich in the desired component.

The corresponding liquid of higher boiling point flows back to the boiling kettle.

Many chemical reactions are carried out in the presence of water, and the desired product is found in solution. Recovery involves the evaporation of the water, a step resembling distillation, except that one component, the salt, is not volatile. The evaporation may take place in a pan over a fire, or in an open tank in which steam coils are immersed. These are not economical of fuel, but they may be the only practicable means. In many cases special equipment for evaporation may be used, with high economy of fuel.

Multiple evaporation. It is possible to use the steam of one evaporation so as to further another evaporation. As many as a dozen units may be connected in series, most installations using three or four. The problem is one of obtaining the required temperature differences between the units so that the vapor from one is at a higher temperature than the boiling point of the liquid in the next unit. This is usually accomplished by operating the unit that receives the fresh live steam from the boiler at a higher pressure, and maintaining the last unit in the series under vacuum. Each unit of such a multiple-effect evaporator evaporates a little less than an additional pound of water for the pound of live steam introduced into the first effect.

For carrying out the many chemical reactions a wide variety of equipment is used. This may be a simple open tank, or a complicated apparatus capable of withstanding pressures of thousands of pounds per square inch. The materials of construction are chosen to resist the corrosive action of the chemicals under treatment. Those for the production of fine chemicals are of stainless steel, or of iron or steel with a lining of fused enamel or glass. For heating, the containers may be jacketed, and steam or hot oil introduced into the jacket; often submerged pipes are used. For low temperatures, refrigerated brine is circulated through the jacket or coils.

Thorough mixing of the contents is often necessary. Mechanical agitators are of various forms, for they may have to handle thick doughy masses. An air or steam jet is sometimes introduced directly. In other cases, to grind off coatings and expose fresh surfaces, the whole container is mounted on trunnions and rotated.

The whole industrial chemical equipment is designed to perform these simple unit processes. There are naturally many modifications of the simple devices described above, aimed to increase their efficiency in special processes. It is the function of the chemical engineer to select the equipment best fitted to the task at hand, to choose apparatus of proper capacity, to provide means of feeding and of taking away products, to add the necessary control equipment. The choice of materials to resist corrosion is a most important detail. Yet all traces back to the research laboratory and some early experiment carried out in a bit of glassware, out of which were developed the process and all the engineering data from which the plant was designed.

The names of chemical compounds, many of them long and cumbersome, puzzle the average reader. The difficulty sometimes lies in the fact that the industry uses a dual nomenclature. Many compounds retain their Latin names, or derivatives of these; this is particularly true of drugs. For example "saltpeter" (scientific name, potassium nitrate, KNO_3) is derived from the medieval Latin *sal petrae*, salt of rock. It occurs as an incrustation on the rocks of caves. Epsom salt (magnesium sulphate, $MgSO_4 \cdot 7\,H_2O$) is named after the town of Epsom, England, where it was found in medicinal waters. Glauber salt (sodium sulphate, $Na_2SO_4 \cdot 10\,H_2O$) is named after a German industrial chemist of the seventeenth century.

The modern scientific method is to embody in the name of a chemical compound some idea of its chemical composition. The names of metallic compounds containing only oxygen are compounded of the name of the elemental metal with *oxide*. Where two valences are involved so that there are two oxides possible, the suffix *-ous* is attached to the metal name to designate the oxide of lower valence; the suffix *-ic*, to indicate the higher valence. For example, there are a lower oxide of iron, ferrous oxide, FeO, and a higher oxide, ferric oxide, Fe_2O_3. The same system applies to the hydroxides in which the group —OH is attached to the metal: for example, sodium hydroxide, NaOH; aluminum hydroxide, $Al(OH)_3$.

The salts are composed of a metallic or basic unit and an acid unit. Their names also consist of two parts, one indicative of the element, the other of the acid component. A table of some of the more common acids and the designation of the derived salts follows:

Acid	Formula	Salt
Hydrochloric	HCl	Chloride
Hypochlorous	$HClO$	Hypochlorite
Chloric	$HClO_3$	Chlorate
Perchloric	$HClO_4$	Perchlorate
Hydrosulphurous	H_2S	Sulphide
Sulphurous	H_2SO_3	Sulphite
Sulphuric	H_2SO_4	Sulphate
Nitrous	HNO_2	Nitrite
Nitric	HNO_3	Nitrate
Metasilicic	H_2SiO_3	Metasilicate
Orthosilicic	H_4SiO_4	Orthosilicate
Phosphorous	H_3PO_3	Phosphite
Metaphosphoric	HPO_3	Metaphosphate
Orthophosphoric	H_3PO_4	Orthophosphate
Pyrophosphoric	$H_4P_2O_7$	Pyrophosphate
Carbonic	H_2CO_3	Carbonate

An acid such as orthophosphoric with three replaceable hydrogen atoms, may have three sodium salts, depending on the number replaced: monosodium orthophosphate, NaH_2PO_4, disodium orthophosphate, Na_2HPO_4, and trisodium orthophosphate, Na_3PO_4.

The nomenclature of inorganic chemistry cannot be used with the many times more numerous organic compounds, for these are all carbon compounds, and the name "carbon" would permit no differentiation. A dual system also is found in this division, many names being arbitrary in derivation. In 1892 an International Congress of Chemists met in Switzerland, and established a rational system of naming organic compounds, which permits derivation of their composition, similar to that in mineral chemistry.

An example of the old and the new system is the following: Aniline is a well known, essential material for the production of the aniline dyes. It was originally extracted from anil, a tropical plant;

hence its name. Its constitution is represented by its formula, $C_6H_5 \cdot NH_2$, indicating a fundamental C_6H_5— (which the International Congress called the phenyl group) and a functional group NH_2— (which it called the amine group). Thus the scientific name of aniline would be phenylamine.

The aliphatic, or straight-chain, hydrocarbons are:

Methane	CH	Butane	C_4H_{10}
Ethane	C_2H_6	Pentane	C_5H_{12}
Propane	C_3H_8	Hexane	C_6H_{14}

The succeeding members take the Greek names for the numerals indicating the number of carbon atoms. When they enter combination with a functional group the names replace the suffix *-ane* with the new suffix *-yl;* in combination, ethane becomes ethyl. The olefines have the same prefix as the saturated series above, but the suffix becomes *-ene* instead of *-ane*. Thus the olefine with three carbon atoms becomes propene. When they enter into combinations the suffix becomes *-enyl* or *-ynyl* as euphony requires. Thus ethylene, $CH_2:CH_2$ in combination as $CH_2:CH$— is ethenyl, though this particular group is often called vinyl. The position of the double bond in these hydrocarbons is important, and it is customary to indicate the carbon atom to which it is attached by prefixing its Arabic number to the name; thus, CH_3—$CH:CH$—CH— is 2-butenyl. With two double bonds, as $CH_2:CH$—$CH:CH$— is 1,3-butadienyl.

In the case of a branched-chain hydrocarbon, for example,

$$CH_3CHCH_2CH_3$$
$$|$$
$$CH_3$$

this formula may be written $CH_3CH(CH_3)CH_2CH_3$, the parentheses denoting that the methyl group is in a side chain attached to the preceding carbon atom, and the name is 2-methylbutane. The numbering of the carbon atoms begins nearest the functional group, if present, and always in such a manner as to obtain the lowest possible numbers.

Ring systems are catalogued in the several handbooks dealing with chemical compounds.

Here is a list of the common functional groups which are attached to the parent hydrocarbons, and the suffixes used to indicate them:

Group Name	Formula	Suffix
Alcohol	—OH	-ol
Acid	—COOH	-oic, -oyl
Aldehyde	—CHO	-al
Amine	—NH₂	-amine
Double bond	: or =	-ene
Ketone	: CO	-one
Mercaptan	—SH	-thiol
Nitrile	—CN	nitrile
Sulphonic derivatives	—HSO₃	sulphonate
Triple bond	: or ≡	-yne

The common propyl alcohol, $CH_3CH_2CH_2OH$, is propenol. Butyric acid, which gives the objectionable odor to rancid butter, is $CH_3CH_2CH_2COOH$, and should strictly be called butanoic acid.

An aromatic such as benzene, C_6H_6, has six hydrogen atoms which may be replaced by functional groups. If only one is concerned it does not matter which hydrogen atom is replaced, for they are all identical. But if two are replaced three different isomers are possible. In this case it is customary to number the hydrogen atoms from one to six, clockwise, starting at the top. If two hydrogens in benzene are replaced by chlorine to form dichlorbenzene, there are three possible combinations:

Old System	New System
Orthodichlorbenzene	1,2-dichlorbenzene
Metadichlorbenzene	1,3-dichlorbenzene
Paradichlorbenzene	1,4-dichlorbenzene

The numbers in the new system indicate the hydrogen atoms replaced by the chlorine.

Among the common hydrocarbon groups whose common names do not follow exact scientific nomenclature are:

Prefix	Formula	Prefix	Formula
Acetyl	$CH_3CO—$	Benzal	C_6H_5CH:
Allyl	$CH_2:CHCH_2—$	Benzenyl	C_6H_5C :
Amyl	$C_5H_{11}—$	Benzoyl	$C_6H_5CO—$
Anilino	$C_6H_5NH—$	Benzyl	$C_6H_5CH_2—$
Azo, diazo	—N:N—	Carbonyl	OC:

Prefix	Formula	Prefix	Formula
Carbyl	—C—	Nitroso	—NO
Ethoxy	CH_3CH_2O—	Phenoxy	C_6H_5O—
Ethylidine	CH_3CH:	Phenyl	C_6H_5—
Formyl	HCO—	Phenylene	C_6H_4:
Imino	NH:	Pyridil	C_5H_4N—
Malonyl	—$OCCH_2CO$—	Styryl	$C_6H_5CH_2CH$—
Methylene	—CH_2—	Sulpho	—HSO_3
Methylidine	CH :	Sulphonamido	—SO_2NH—
Naphthal	$C_{10}H_5CH$:	Thio	—S—
Naphthyl	$C_{10}H_7$—	Tolyl	$CH_3C_6H_4$—
Nitramino	—$HNNO_2$	Vinyl	CH_2:CH—
Nitro	—NO_2	Vinylene	—CH:CH—

It is recognized that this is only a very brief summary of the important subject of nomenclature. There are dozens of pages of rules, and long lists of special compounds. Reference should be made to any of the numerous textbooks on organic chemistry for a more complete treatment.

INDEX

235